ORGANIC CHEMISTRY EXPERIMENTS

LABORATORY MANUAL

(CHM 2210L AND 2211L)

Compiled by
the Chemistry Faculty at Miami Dade College (North Campus)

D1377429

Aglob Publishing

Published by: **Aglob Publishing**
Hallandale Beach, Florida
Tel: 954-456-1476
www.aglobpublishing.com

This edition was published from the authors' manuscript copy

Library of Congress Control Number: 2004110243

ISBN: 1-59427-033-3

Manufactured in the United States of America

5 4 3 2 1

SPECIAL PRECAUTIONS TO BE FOLLOWED
WHEN USING ORGANIC REAGENTS.

I. ALL ORGANIC REAGENTS SHOULD BE HANDLED AS IF THEY A HAZARDOUS, FLAMMABLE AND HIGHLY TOXIC! IT IS THEREFORE IMPORTANT TO WORK WITH THEM IN THE FUME HOODS AS MUCH AS IS POSSIBLE. THEY SHOULD BE KEPT AWAY FROM OPEN FLAMES UNLESS SPECIFICALLY INDICATED IN THE EXPERIMENTAL PROCEDURE AND SPECIAL CARE SHOULD BE TAKEN TO AVOID CONTACT WITH SKIN.

II. READ ALL LABELS CAREFULLY! BE SURE THAT YOU ARE USING THE CORRECT CHEMICAL IN THE CORRECT CONCENTRATION.

III. BE SURE TO COVER ALL REAGENT BOTTLES AND OTHER CONTAINERS AFTER USING THEM!

IV. DISPENSING CONTAINERS SUCH AS BEAKERS AND MEASURING CYLINDERS, AND TRANSFERRING DEVICES SUCH AS DROPPERS SYRINGES AND SPATULAS, ARE PROVIDED FOR EACH REAGENT. ALL OF THESE CONTAINERS AND TRANSFERRING DEVICES WILL BE PROPERLY LABELED AND PLACED IN A LOGICAL ORDER FOR EACH LAB EXPERIMENT.

     a) DO NOT REMOVE ANY REAGENT BOTTLES, DISPENSING CONTAINERS OR TRANSFERRING DEVICES FROM THE HOOD UNLESS SPECIFICALLY TOLD TO DO SO!

     b) DO NOT MOVE BOTTLES OR CONTAINERS FROM ONE PLACE IN THE HOOD TO THE ANOTHER!

     c) DO NOT MOVE DROPPERS, SYRINGES OR SPATULAS FROM ONE PLACE IN THE HOOD TO ANOTHER!

     d) BE SURE TO REPLACE DROPPERS AND OTHER TRANSFERRING DEVICES IN THEIR APPROPRIATE, LABELED CONTAINERS AFTER USE!

     e) NEVER LEAVE DROPPERS, SYRINGES OR SPATULAS LYING ON THE SURFACE OF THE HOOD! REPLACE IN APPROPRIATE CONTAINERS TO AVOID CONTAMINATION!

     f) DO NOT PLACE DROPPERS OR SYRINGES DIRECTLY IN REAGENT BOTTLES! ONLY IN THE DISPENSING CONTAINERS PROVIDED!

     g) DO NOT PLACE ANY ADDITIONAL DROPPERS, SYRINGES, SPATULAS, BEAKERS OR MEASURING CYLINDERS IN THIS HOOD! USE ONLY THOSE PROPERLY LABELED ONES PROVIDED!

     h) NEVER POUR CHEMICALS FROM YOUR APPARATUS BACK INTO THE ORIGINAL REAGENT BOTTLES! EITHER TRANSFER EXCESS BACK TO THE DISPENSING CONTAINER PROVIDED OR DISCARD IN ORGANIC WASTE JAR IF THERE IS EVEN THE SLIGHTEST CHANCE THAT THE CHEMICAL MAY HAVE BEEN CONTAMINATED.

NOTE:

THESE PRECAUTIONS ARE BEING LISTED FOR YOUR OWN SAFETY, AS WELL AS FOR THE SAFE AND ACCURATE RUNNING OF EACH EXPERIMENT. REMEMBER ALSO THAT THESE ARE MICROSCALE EXPERIMENTS WHICH HAVE BEEN DESIGNED TO MINIMIZE CHEMICAL WASTE.

CRYSTAL FORMATION

Formation of crystalline product is the desired result of many chemical reactions. This is particularly so in derivative preparation. When derivatives are prepared, most procedures discuss purification and analysis of product crystals in great detail. However, what can be done if crystals DO NOT FORM when a procedure indicates that they should?

The procedures in preparing a derivative follow a general pattern which is true for MOST, but NOT ALL, possible compounds. Although a procedure might indicate that crystals should form within several minutes, the crystallization process may take several hours or several days. Some crystals form stable supersaturated solutions. Others are formed at a slower rate.

Crystal formation may be hastened or induced by:

(1) scratching the inside of the test tube or flask in which the dissolved crystals are found. Small pieces of glass are stirred into the "mother liquor" and become nuclei for crystal growth.

(2) seed crystals (if available) may be added.

(3) thorough cooling.

(4) evaporation of a portion of the liquid followed by thorough cooling.

(5) addition of a miscible solvent in which product crystals are less soluble.

Any or all of these techniques may be used to encourage the growth of crystals.

RECRYSTALLIZATION

When a crystalline product is obtained, it is often contaminated with unreacted starting materials or side-products. Usually crystals must be purified in order to give good melting points and good spectra. The most common method of purification is RECRYSTALLIZATION. Recrystallization follows the steps outlined below.

(1) The impure crystals (which may be damp) are transferred into a small beaker. (A test tube may be used for very small amounts of solid.)

(2) A small volume, one to two milliliters, of reagent alcohol is added to the beaker.

(3) The mixture of impure crystals and ethanol is warmed gently to dissolve the crystals. If too much alcohol is added, the crystals will dissolve and remain dissolved. If too little alcohol is added, the crystals will not dissolve.

(4) As needed, small increments of ethanol are added until the crystals dissolve in the HOT alcohol.

(5) The hot solution is removed from the heat, allowed to cool undisturbed to room temperature, and then further cooled in ice. At this point, crystals should have formed.

(6) If crystals did not form, some of the alcohol may need to be evaporated. The addition of a small amount of water is acceptable in some cases. Water is much more polar than ethanol and decreases the solubility of the crystals. Because of miscibility, water and ethanol are often paired.

(7) Once crystals form, they are cooled, suction-filtered, and dried.

Reagent alcohol (ethanol) is the most common solvent used for most recrystallizations. However, other solvents such as ether or cyclohexane are also used. In any recrystallization, it is important that some solvent remain once crystals have formed. This "mother liquor" serves to dissolve impurities. If it all evaporates, impurities remain with the crystals.

Table of Contents

EXPERIMENT 1

CALIBRATION OF THE THERMOMETER

Most laboratory thermometers give reproducible readings over their respective ranges. However, these readings often do not correspond to the tabulated values in reference texts. Thus, the reference value for the boiling point of water at 760mmHg is 100°C, but a laboratory thermometer may read 101.5, 99.0, or some other value at this temperature. In order to compare lab measurements with reference values, each thermometer must be calibrated. Calibration involves the comparison of the actual temperature reading obtained under equilibrium conditions with a reference temperature cited for that equilibrium.

Calibration must be done at several different temperatures for each individual thermometer. This is necessary because each thermometer seldom deviates from the reference value by the same quantity at all different temperatures. Specifically, it is important to calibrate the thermometer over the temperature range, which will be used during the laboratory experiments.

The deviation of the laboratory thermometer will be determined at various temperatures in the 0-250°C range. A plot of the actual deviation vs. the true temperature can then be prepared. This will serve as a quick graphical method for adjusting temperatures measured during the laboratory term.

The actual calibration involves the solid/liquid equilibrium, (melting point). Generally, less error occurs in the measurement of a melting point (solid-liquid equilibrium) than that of a boiling point (liquid-gas equilibrium). Unlike boiling points, the melting points of pure substances are not affected to any great extent by changes in the external pressure.

PROCEDURE

To measure melting points, an electric melting point apparatus such as the one pictured next page will be used.

A small sample of the substance whose melting point is to be measured is placed in a capillary tube with one closed end. This is accomplished by tapping the open end of the capillary tube against the sample until 3-5 mm of sample has entered. The tube is then inverted (closed end down) and dropped down a 2-3 foot length of glass tubing on the desk top. The bouncing of the capillary tube against the desk top packs the sample into the closed end of the tube. The sample-filled capillary tube is placed in a sample port of the melting point apparatus. A thermometer whose bulb is no larger than the sample is inserted in the thermometer port. The instrument is turned on and the Variac dial is used to increase the temperature. This Variac dial does not indicate the actual temperature, but represents the % of voltage output.

1. Prepare a capillary sample of each of the pure substances listed.
2. Measure the melting range of each pure substance and record the values on your data sheet.

1...THERMOMETER PORT
2...CAPILLARY SAMPLE PORTS
3...VIEWER
4...HOT STAGE
5...LIGHT SOURCE
6...VARIAC DIAL
7...ON-OFF SWITCH
8...FUSE
9...WIRE TO ELECTRICAL OUTLET

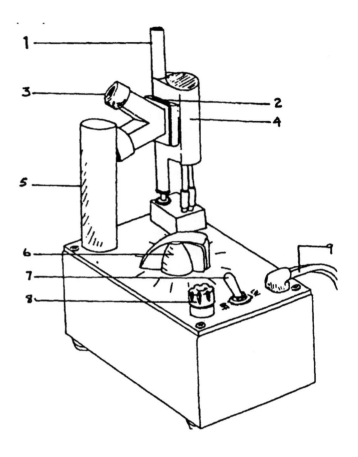

NOTE: Begin with the lowest melting point listed and continue to successively higher and higher melting points. In this fashion, little or no time is required to cool the apparatus between individual melting point determinations.

EXPERIMENT 1: Report and Worksheet

CALIBRATION OF THERMOMETER

Student Name: _____   Day: _____

Student Number: _____   Date: _____

_____

DATA

COMPOUND	Reference M.P.	Observed M.P.	Average Temp.	Deviation
Naphthalene	80 - 82 ºC			
Urea	132 – 133 ºC			
Sulfanilamide	164 – 165 ºC			
4– Toulic acid	180 – 182 ºC			
Anthracene	214 – 217 ºC			

QUESTIONS

1) WHY must a thermometer be calibrated even though it repeatedly gives the same readings?

2) WHY does the melting of a pure substance occur over a melting range rather than at one temperature?

3) EXPLAIN how future thermometer readings must be adjusted based upon the data collected. WHY are numerous readings taken?

MIXED MELTING POINTS: MP UNKNOWN

A melting point measures the equilibrium existing between the solid and the liquid states of any substance. It represents the temperature at which the vapor pressure of the solid equals the vapor pressure of the liquid. This physical constant depends upon the strength of the attractions found within a crystal lattice, but is virtually independent of external pressure. A melting point, however, is greatly affected by the presence of soluble impurities.

A pure substance will melt sharply within a range of: four (4) or fewer degrees Celsius under the conditions of measurement. An impure substance may (a) melt within the same range as a pure substance when the impurity is insoluble in the melted substance, or (b) melt over a broad, lowered range of sometimes as much as 100 degrees Celsius when the impurity dissolves in the melted substance. A soluble impurity causes the melting range to begin well below the true melting point and to be completed before the true melting point is reached.

A simple melting point measurement serves as a good criterion of purity. A sharp melting point is indicative of a pure substance. A broad melting point range indicates contamination by a soluble impurity. Furthermore, when two identical samples are mixed together, there is no change in the melting point or the melting range. If two dissimilar samples are mixed, (even in the case where both samples have the same true melting point), the melting point of the mixture is lowered and the range is greatly increased.

In order to understand why a melting point is altered by the presence of a soluble impurity, it is important to remember that melting occurs when the vapor pressure of the solid phase equals the vapor pressure of the liquid phase. As a small quantity of the solid melts, the liquid becomes saturated with dissolved impurity and the vapor pressure of the liquid is lowered. The actual lowering of the vapor pressure depends upon the mole fraction of the liquid times the vapor pressure of the pure liquid. Thus, a much lower temperature is required for the vapor pressures of the solid and the liquid to be equal, and melting occurs well below the true melting point. This saturated solution also represents the lowest temperature possible for melting to occur and is called the **EUTECTIC TEMPERATURE**, T. As more of the solid melts, the mole fraction of the pure liquid increases, its vapor pressure increases, and a higher temperature is required for further melting. When all of the solid has melted at temperature T, the liquid still contains some dissolved impurity and therefore still has not achieved the vapor pressure of the pure liquid. Thus, the final temperature, T, is still below the melting point of the pure substance.

In summary, the presence of a soluble impurity is shown by a broad melting range and T, - T, is greater than 4°C. Also, the entire mixture melts below the true melting point of the pure substance and T, is less than T_{pure}.

To measure melting points, an electric melting point apparatus such as the one pictured next page below will be used.

1...THERMOMETER PORT
2...CAPILLARY SAMPLE PORTS
3...VIEWER
4...HOT STAGE
5...LIGHT SOURCE
6...VARIAC DIAL
7...ON-OFF SWITCH
8...FUSE
9...WIRE TO ELECTRICAL OUTLET

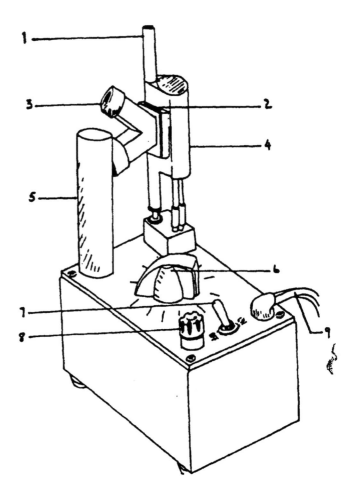

A small sample of the substance whose melting point is to be measured is placed in a capillary tube with one closed end. This is accomplished by tapping the open end of the capillary tube against the sample until 3-5 mm of sample has entered. The tube is then inverted (closed end down) and dropped down a 2-3 foot length of glass tubing on the desk top. The bouncing of the capillary tube against the desk top packs the sample into the closed end of the tube. The sample-filled capillary tube is placed in a sample port of the melting point apparatus. A thermometer whose bulb is no larger than the sample is inserted in the thermometer port. the instrument is turned on and the Variac dial is used to increase the temperature. This Variac dial does not indicate the actual temperature, but represents the % of voltage output.

Several problems arise in measuring melting points in this fashion. The most common mistake involves heating the sample too rapidly. When this is done, the sample melts before equilibration can occur between the sample and the mercury in the thermometer.

To heat the sample very slowly is ideal, but requires much more time than can be readily devoted to obtaining a melting point. The most effective manner of heating a sample is a compromise. The sample is first heated rapidly to about 10 or 15 degrees below the expected melting point and then very slowly at a rate of 2°C per minute, until melting occurs. The initial temperature (T_i) and final temperature (T_f) are recorded. When the melting point of an unknown sample is to be determined, the sample is heated rapidly to obtain an approximate melting point, cooled, then heated slowly and carefully again to repeat the melting point measurement over the final 10-15 degrees.

The major flaw in using an electrical melting point apparatus is that the response time between a change in the Variac reading and a temperature change is very slow. For example, increasing the Variac dial from 40 to 50 may not show the full effect on the temperature for 5 minutes; and once a high temperature As reached, the apparatus is very slow to cool down. Practice will be required before a good technique can be established to obtain accurate melting points in relatively short time periods.

PROCEDURE

1. Prepare capillary samples of pure urea and cinnamic acid, and also of the various mixtures of these solids in the ratios listed.

2. Measure the melting range of each pure substance and mixture. Record these values on the data sheet.

3. Obtain an unknown sample from the instructor and determine its melting range. (The unknown is from the list of substances provided.)

4. Mix the unknown with a pure sample of the substance on the list which you suspect it to be and determine the melting range of this mixture.

5. Record all measurements on the data sheet and identify the unknown.

<u>EXPERIMENT 2: Report and Worksheet</u>

MIXED MELTING POINTS: MP UNKNOWN

Student Name: _____   Day: _____

Student Number: _____   Date: _____

_____

DATA

UNKNOWN NUMBER: _____

SAMPLE	Ref. M.P.	Observed M.P.
pure urea	132-133 ºC	
pure cinnamic acid	132-133 ºC	
mixture (1:4)	. . . .	
mixture (1:1)	. . . .	
mixture (4:1)	. . . .	
pure unknown	. . . .	
Unknown + ( )	. . . .	

IDENTIFY UNKNOWN: _____

QUESTIONS

1. What is the EUTECTIC TEMPERATURE?

2. EXPLAIN the observed melting ranges and melting points of the three mixtures tested. What, in general, is the effect of a soluble impurity on the melting point and the melting range of a compound?

BOILING POINT/REFRACTIVE INDEX

Boiling points of pure substances depend on external pressure, (pressure is directly proportional to the absolute temperature) and thus boiling points vary slightly according to the barometric pressure at which they are determined.

To measure boiling points, the test tube method will be used. This requires a small amount of liquid (2-5 mL) and gives good results in most instances. The liquid is placed in a clean dry test tube, several boiling chips are added, and a thermometer is suspended approximately 1/3 to 1/2 inch above the liquid. **The top of the test tube must be kept open during the boiling process to prevent a buildup of pressure**. The thermometer is NOT inserted directly into the boiling liquid because most liquids superheat during the boiling process.

As each liquid boils, vapor rises above the liquid, condenses, and then drips back into the boiling liquid. This equilibrium between liquid and vapor represents the TRUE boiling temperature as indicated by that specific thermometer. In most liquids, a visible ring of condensing vapor will be formed which will rise as more heat is applied. When this ring covers the entire thermometer bulb and the bulb drips with condensing liquid, equilibrium is established and this temperature represents the correct boiling point for the liquid. As the first vapors hit the bulb of the thermometer, the mercury in the thermometer will rise quickly. As equilibrium is achieved, no further rise in the mercury level will occur, the temperature will remain constant, and the boiling point can be measured.

The other physical constant of a liquid which is most convenient to measure in the laboratory is its refractive index. The refractive index is a measure of the degree to which light will bend as it passes through a sample relative to the degree to which it will bend in a vacuum or in air. The degree of bending or refraction is dependent on the velocity with which the light travels in the particular material. This is in turn dependent on the density of the material and the denser something is, the slower the velocity of light as it passes through it. The refractive index, n, is expressed as:

$$\frac{\text{velocity of a vacuum}}{\text{velocity in sample}} = n \text{ (refractive index)}$$

Since all materials measured will have a greater density than that of a vacuum, the refractive index is always greater than 1.

Typically the refractive index is measured at 20°C. Since the density of a material varies with temperature, the velocity of light passing through a material would also be altered by fluctuating temperatures. The refractive index is also very sensitive to the presence of impurities and, as a result, can be a very useful tool in monitoring the purification of liquid samples.

PROCEDURE

Assemble the equipment shown inside the HOOD. This equipment will be used for each of the boiling point determinations. Once the assembly has been arranged, have it checked by your instructor.

BOILING POINT APPARATUS:

1...THERMOMETER ADAPTER: used
     to hold the thermometer (clamped)
2...THERMOMETER: correct range must
     be visible.
3...RING STAND: supports all equipment
4...TEST TUBE: clamped just below the
     lip to prevent slipping; open at
     the top to allow for rising vapors;
     1mL of liquid + boiling chip.
5...BULB OF THERMOMETER: 1/2 inch
     above liquid.

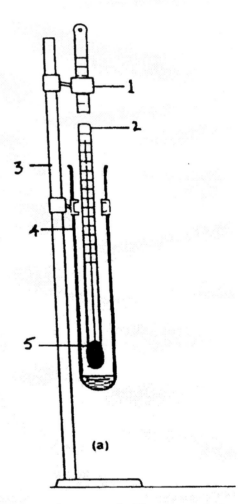

(a)

1. Measure the refractive index of each substance to be tested. The use of the refractometer will be demonstrated by the instructor.
2. Place approximately **1mL** of the known liquid and a boiling chip in a clean, dry test tube. Clamp the tube into the assembly.
3. Using the burner, **CAUTIOUSLY** heat the liquid. When too much heat is applied, the vapor ring rises higher and higher. If this vapor ring escapes from the test tube, it **CATCHES ON FIRE OR EXPLODES! Remember most organic liquids are highly flammable.**
4. Observe the formation of the vapor ring, and the temperature (constant) at which the liquid boils. Record this temperature on your data sheet.
5. After the boiling point determination, discard each organic liquid IN THE ORGANIC WASTE CONTAINER provided for that purpose.

LIST OF UNKNOWNS FOR
BOILING POINTS, IR
AND NMR ANALYSIS

NAME OF COMPOUND	B.P.	DENSITY	R.I.	TYPE
ethyl acetate	77	0.901	1.3720	ester
butanone	80	-	1.3791	ketone
2-propanol	83	0.785	1.3793	alcohol
t-butanol	83	0.779	1.3878	alcohol
2-methyl-3-butanone	94	-	1.3879	ketone
1-propanol	97	0.804	1.3850	alcohol
2-butanol	99	0.807	1.3950	alcohol
1-bromobutane	100	1.274	1.4400	halide
2-pentanone	102	0.806	1.3902	ketone
3-pentanone	102	-	1.3905	ketone
pinacolone	106	-	1.3960	ketone
toluene	111	0.867	1.4961	Ar-R
4-methyl-2-pentanone	116	-	1.3956	ketone
1-butanol	116	0.820	1.3974	alcohol
2,4-dimethyl-3-pentanone	124	-	1.3999	ketone
3-hexanone	125	-	1.4007	ketone
2-hexanone	128	-	1.4007	ketone
cyclopentanone	131	-	1.4366	ketone
hexanal	131	-	1.4068	aldehyde
chlorobenzene	132	1.107	1.525	Ar-X
p-xylene	137	0.861	1.4958	Ar-R
2-hexanol	139	0.810	1.4186	alcohol
4-heptanone	144	-	1.4069	ketone
3-heptanone	148	-	1.4092	ketone
2-heptanone	151	-	1.4007	ketone
anisole	154	0.994	1.5221	ether
heptanal	155	-	1.4125	aldehyde
cyclohexanone	156	-	1.4507	ketone
o-chlorotoluene	159	1.082	1.5240	Ar-X
p-chlorotoluene	162	1.071	1.5210	Ar-X
octanal	171	-	1.4217	aldehyde
phenetole	172	0.967	1.5080	ether
2-octanone	173	-	1.4152	ketone
1-heptanol	176	0.822	1.4245	alcohol
benzaldehyde	179	-	1.5446	aldehyde
benzyl chloride	179	1.100	1.5390	halide
2-octanol	179	0.821	1.4265	alcohol
aniline	184	1.022	1.5863	amine
benzylamine	184	0.984	1.5401	amine
nonanal	185	-	1.4273	aldehyde
N,N-dimethylaniline	193	0.956	1.5582	amine
phenylacetaldehyde	194	-	1.5319	aldehyde
2-nonanone	195	-	1.4207	ketone
methylaniline	196	0.989	1.5730	amine

List of Unknowns (Cont.)

NAME OF COMPOUND	B.P.	DENSITY	R.I.	TYPE
phenyl acetate	196	1.078	1.503	ester
o-toluidine	199	1.005	1.5688	amine
acetophenone	202	1.028	1.5339	ketone
p-tolualdehyde	204	-	1.5454	aldehyde
benzyl alcohol	205	1.045	1.5396	alcohol
N-ethylaniline	205	0.962	1.5559	amine
nitrobenzene	210	1.203	1.5530	$Ar-NO_2$
2-chlorobenzaldehyde	213	-	1.5671	halide
ethyl benzoate	213	1.047	1.5057	ester
propiophenone	218	-	1.5270	ketone
isobutyrophenone	222	-	1.5190	ketone
n-butyrophenone	230	-	1.5196	ketone
p-anisaldehyde	242	-	1.5731	aldehyde
cinnamaldehyde	252	-	1.6195	aldehyde

EXPERIMENT 3: Report and Worksheet

BOILING POINT/REFRACTIVE INDEX

Student Name: _____   Day: _____

Student Number: _____   Date: _____

DATA

UNKNOWN NUMBER:_____

COMPOUND	B. P. Ref.	B. P. Obs.	R. I. Ref.	R. I. Obs.
butanone	80 •C		1.3791	
2-propanol	83 •C		1.3793	
2-butanol	98 -C		1.3950	
benzaldehyde	178 °C		1.5463	
UNKNOWN COMPOUND	-------		-------	

IDENTITY OF UNKNOWN:_____

QUESTIONS

1) When a B.P. is measured, WHY is it important that the tube is vented?

2) What factors affect the B.P. of a pure compound?

3) The reference R.I. values are usually obtained at 20'C. What happens to the R.I. reading if the temperature is above 20'C? What happens if the temperature is below 20'C?

DISTILLATION

One of the most convenient methods used to separate a miscible mixture (a solution) of volatile liquids which have different boiling points is termed DISTILLATION. Distillation involves boiling the volatile mixture and condensing the vapors produced. Simple distillation can effectively separate liquids whose boiling points differ by 80 degrees or more, while Fractional distillation can be adapted to separate liquids whose boiling point difference may be as small as 0.10°C.

When a solution is composed of two or more volatile, miscible liquids, the boiling point of that solution lies somewhere between the highest boiling and the lowest boiling constituents. Recall that boiling occurs when the vapor pressure of the mixture equals external pressure. Consider a solution composed of one mole of liquid A, boiling at 60°C, and one mole of liquid B, boiling at 160°C. The vapor pressure of the solution at any specific temperature is the sum of the vapor pressure of liquid A and that of liquid B, i.e. $^{v}p_{solution} = {}^{v}p_{A} + {}^{v}p_{B}$. The vapor pressure of liquid A is represented by its mole fraction multiplied by vapor pressure of pure liquid A at that specific temperature:

$$^{v}p_{A,} = (X_{A})\,({}^{v}p_{Ao})$$

AND: $$^{v}p_{B} = (X_{B})\,({}^{v}p_{Bo})$$

When the sum of these vapor pressures equals 760mm, (or whatever the external pressure may be), the solution boils. This occurs at a temperature which depends upon the composition of the solution and the boiling points of the individual liquids.

When the mixture boils, the vapor produced has a different composition than the boiling liquid. Liquid A has a lower boiling point and a higher vapor pressure than liquid B at any given temperature. The vapor will contain a greater fraction of A molecules and a lesser fraction of B molecules. Thus the vapor contains a higher concentration of the more volatile component. Cooling the vapor to the liquid state produces a liquid which has a higher mole fraction of A and a lower mole fraction of B. This new liquid boils at a lower temperature because of its new composition. If this process of heating and condensing is repeated many times, the vapor resulting from the final heating will be essentially pure A, the more volatile, lower-boiling component of the original solution.

Fractional distillation enables a large number of vapor-liquid equilibria to occur. Each of the many vaporization-condensation processes serves to enrich the distillate (substance condensed in the final phase) in the more volatile component. In practice, the mixture to be distilled is placed in a boiling flask along with several boiling chips. A distilling column, placed directly above the boiling flask, gives a large surface area in which the vapor-liquid equilibria may occur. Collection of the distillate and monitoring of the temperature involves use of the distilling head, thermometer, adapter, condenser and receiver.

Heat for the distillation is usually supplied by a Bunsen burner, an electric heating mantle or, (particularly in microscale organic experiments), by an electric sand bath. The bulb of the thermometer is placed just below the side-arm leading to the condenser. This insures correct temperature readings of the distillate. The condenser, usually supplied with running water, cools the vapors that reach the top of the distilling column and allows them to be collected in a collecting flask.

As the mixture in the distilling flask boils, a vapor forms directly above the liquid which is in equilibrium with the liquid.. The vapor cools and condenses, dripping back toward the boiling liquid. As this condensed liquid drips back toward the boiling liquid, it is struck by fresh hot ascending vapor. The transfer of heat from the hot ascending vapor causes the cooler descending liquid to revaporize, and a new vapor-liquid equilibrium is established. The revaporized liquid is again richer in the more volatile component. Thus, the length of the distilling column represents the surface area on which many equilibria between descending cooled liquid and ascending hot vapor can occur. Each successive equilibrium further enriches the vapor in the more volatile component. Finally, the vapor at the top of the column (highly enriched in the more volatile component) is cooled and condensed by water running through the outer jacket of the condenser. This distillate is essentially the more volatile component in pure form.

The thermometer is used to measure the temperature of the vapor-liquid equilibrium at the top of the column, not the temperature of the boiling liquid. The observed temperature is indicative of the relative composition of the distillate. If the temperature reading is 61°C, the condensed material is essentially .pure liquid A (B.P. = 60°C) If the temperature reading is 80°C, the distillate of condensed vapors represents some combination of liquid A and a smaller amount of liquid B (whose B.P. = 160°C) . The higher the temperature reading obtained at the top of the column, the greater the proportion of the less volatile component in the distillate.

The best separation is obtained when many vapor-liquid equilibria occur, each enhancing the vapor in the more volatile component. To increase the number of vapor-liquid equilibria occurring, several options are available: A longer distilling column gives a greater surface area for the cooling-reheating process to occur; Packing a distilling column with glass beads or copper sponge also increases the surface area for heat exchange and increases the number of equilibria. Altering the size or changing the packing of a distilling column is one way to obtain a more effective distillation. Another way to increase the number of vapor-liquid equilibria in a distillation is to increase the temperature very slowly. This allows more equilibria to occur within a smaller surface area. Usually, very slow heating consumes too much time so a compromise is effected between the amount of surface area provided for heat exchange and the rate of heating. The usual preferred rate of heating with most distilling apparatus allows for the distillate to be formed at a rate of one drop per second.

A graphical representation of temperature vs. composition for the sample mixture of liquids a (1 mole, 60°C) and B (1 mole, 160°C) is given below. In this example, a mixture consisting of one mole of A and one mole of B boils at approximately 100°C based upon the intercept of the 0.50/0.50 composition with the liquid temperature. The vapor formed at 100°C has a different composition than the boiling liquid. It is richer in the more volatile component. However, since the vapor is in equilibrium with the boiling liquid, it is at the same temperature as the boiling liquid. The composition of the vapor may be found by looking at the vapor line at a temperature of 100°C. When this vapor condenses, it becomes liquid of the same composition. The new composition of the condensed vapor is obtained by a vertical intercept between the vapor curve and the liquid curve. Based on the graph, this new liquid contains about 0.75 X_A and 0.25 X_B.

COMPOSITION VS. BOILING POINT

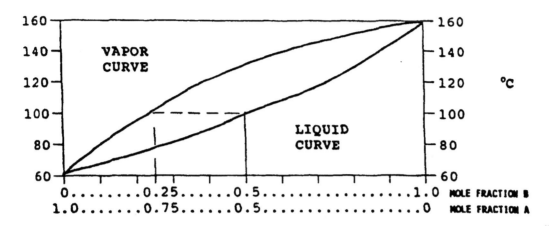

As the liquid is revaporized, it is again in equilibrium with vapor of the same temperature but of different composition, connected by a horizontal line between the liquid and vapor curves. A vertical line connecting the vapor to liquid of the same composition represents the condensation process. Horizontal lines connecting the vapor and liquid compositions indicate an equilibrium existing between liquid of one composition and vapor of a different composition.

A summary can be made of the physical processes occurring within a distilling column during a distillation. As the hot vapor travels up the column, it is continually condensed and revaporized. Each equilibrium enriches the vapor in the more volatile component and the temperature required to revaporize the condensed vapor continually decreases. Thus, a temperature gradient exists. Going from the top to the bottom of the column, the mixture is less and less rich in the more volatile component.

The physical processes occurring within the boiling flask may also be summarized. As the more volatile component is continually lost, the residue becomes richer and richer in the less volatile component and the boiling point of the mixture increases.

Sometimes, mixtures of liquids form AZEOTROPIC solutions An azeotropic mixture boils at a constant temperature with two or more solutes evaporating at a constant mole ratio. Thus, when a constant boiling point is achieved during a distillation, this may represent either a pure liquid or an azeotropic mixture. Azeotropic mixtures are sometimes nuisances in distillation. At other times they allow certain separations to be performed more easily.

PROCEDURE

PART A; SIMPLE DISTILLATION

Pour 2.0mL of acetone and 2.0mL of deionized water into a 5- mL long-necked, round-bottomed flask. Add a boiling chip. Connect the flask to a sidearm connector using the rubber adapter with the extension arm for clamping to the ring stand. Fit the other end of the connector with a thermometer and thermometer adapter. Be sure that the bulb of the thermometer is just below the sidearm of the connector so that it records the temperature of the rising vapor. Connect the sidearm to a water-jacketed condenser. Clamp the entire assembly with the round-bottomed flask sitting in a sandbath. For collection of the distillate, lead the condenser into a 2-dram vial resting in a 30-mL beaker filled with ice.

Gradually increase the temperature. Once boiling begins, adjust the rate of heating so that no more than about four or five drops of distillate forms per minute. Once the thermometer reads 62°C interrupt heating and measure the volume of distillate produced.

Resume heating until the thermometer reads 95°C. Discontinue heating and measure the volume of distillate produced between 62 and 95°C. Record these measurements on your data sheet along with the volume of the residue remaining in the distilling flask.

APPARATUS FOR SIMPLE DISTILLATION:

1....THERMOMETER
2....THERMOMETER "ADAPTER
3....SIDEARM CONNECTOR
4....WATER OUTLET
5....WATER INLET
6....CONDENSER
7....S-BL LONG KECKED FLASK
8....SAND BATH
9....COLLECTING VIAL
10...30-N. BEAKER WITH ICE

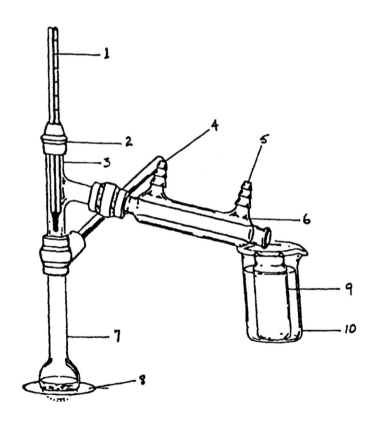

PART B; FRACTIONAL DISTILLATION

Repeat the entire procedure used in PART A but this time pack the neck of the round-bottomed flask with copper sponge. Again measure the volume of distillate produced at the specified temperatures as well as the volume of the remaining residue. Compare these results with those obtained in PART A.

APPARATUS FOR FRACTIONAL DISTILLATION:

1....THERMOMETER
2....THERMOMETER ADAPTER
3. SIDEARM CONNECTOR
4. WATER OUTLET
5....WATER INLET
6....CONDENSER
7....COPPER SPOMCE
8....5-ml LONG NECKED FLASK
9....SAND BATH
10...COLLECTING VIAL
11...30-ml BEAKER WITH ICE

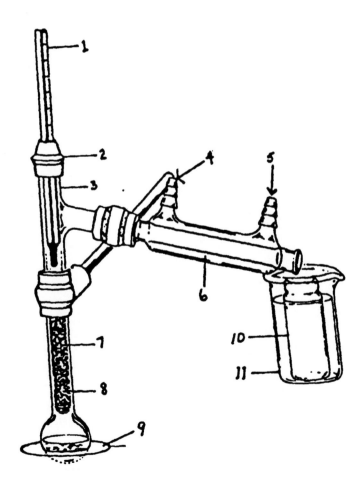

EXPERIMENT 4: Report and Worksheet

DISTILLATION

Student Name: _____   Day: _____

Student Number: _____   Date: _____

DATA

1. PRELIMINARY MEASUREMENTS:

volume of acetone used _____ Ml   volume of water _____ mL

2. DISTILLATION PERFORMED: (check one)   _ Simple   _ Fractional

3. DISTILLATION DATA

TEMPERATURE RANGE	DROPS COLLECTED
to 60	
60 - 95	
residue	

QUESTIONS

1) Compare the results of simple and fractional distillation.

2) How is the effectiveness of a distillation changed by each of the following?

   a) Rapid heating.

   b) Selecting liquids with identical boiling points.

   c) Using a long packed column.

   d) Using a short unpacked column,

3) Explain how the composition of the column material varies from the bottom to the top of the distilling column.

EXTRACTION

Another convenient method used to separate organic mixtures is termed EXTRACTION. This technique uses a solute which has a different solubility in each of two immiscible solvents. When a solute is dissolved in water (or some other solvent) and mixed with an immiscible second solvent, the solute distributes between the two immiscible phases in proportion to its solubility in each solvent. This distribution is measured by a constant, K_D, the distribution coefficient.

$$K_D = \frac{C_{organic}}{C_{water}} = \frac{\text{solute concentration in organic layer}}{\text{solute concentration in water layer}}$$

AND SINCE $\qquad C = \dfrac{\text{grams of solute}}{\text{volume of solvent}} \qquad = \text{concentration}$

$$K_D = \frac{g_{solute\ in\ organic\ layer} / V_{organic\ layer}}{g_{solute\ in\ water} / V_{water\ layer}}$$

When a solute is twice as soluble in a given volume of organic solvent than in an equal volume of water, $K_D = 2$. The greater the distribution coefficient, the more solute can be extracted from the water layer using equal volumes of solvents. Because of the nature of the distribution coefficient, multiple extractions using small volumes of organic solvent are more efficient than a single large volume extraction. This is demonstrable by experiment and by calculation. Once extraction has been completed, the solvents can be separated from each other since they are immiscible and a phase boundary exists between them.

Often mixtures of organic compounds are quite soluble in an organic solvent such as ether and virtually insoluble in water. The distribution coefficient in such cases approaches infinity. If the organic compounds can be converted to ionic species which displays the opposite solubility (that is, the distribution coefficient is approximately zero with the ionic solute soluble in water but insoluble in the organic solvent) then effective separations are possible.

Weak organic bases of 5 or more carbons are usually soluble in organic solvents like ether but insoluble in water. Weak organic bases (RNH_2) may be separated from the neutral or acidic compounds by extraction with aqueous strong acid solutions. The mixture to be separated is first dissolved in some appropriate organic solvent. Addition of aqueous Hcl converts the weak organic base to its water-soluble salt:

$$H^+ + RNH_2 = RNH_3^+$$

After the separation of layers, the weak base can be recovered from the aqueous layer by the addition of some strong base such as NaOH:

$$NaOH + RNH_3^+ = RNH_2 + H_2O + Na^+$$

The organic amine separates from the water layer as an insoluble liquid layer or as a precipitate.

Carboxylic acids (RCOOH) of 5 or more carbons and phenols (ArOH) are quite soluble in organic solvents and insoluble in water. Carboxylic acids and phenols, however, react with strong bases to form ionic, water-soluble salts:

$$RCOOH + NaOH = RCOONa + H_2O$$

$$ArOH + NaOH = ArONa + H_2O$$

Only carboxylic acids are strong enough (pka $\approx$ 5) to react with weaker bases such as NaHCO$_3$ (pka $\approx$ 7)

$$RCOOH + NaHCO_3 = CO_2 + H_2O + RCOO^-Na^+$$

Phenols (pka $\approx$ 9) are not capable of reacting with NaHCO$_3$ (they are weaker acids than H$_2$CO$_3$)

A mixture consisting of a carboxylic acid and any neutral organic compound may be separated by extraction with aqueous NaHCO$_3$ followed by extraction with aqueous NaOH.

The mixture is first dissolved in ether (or any suitable organic solvent). The resulting solution is then extracted by adding a volume of aqueous NaHCO$_3$ which converts the unionized carboxylic acid to its water-soluble salt. The neutral component and the weaker acid, phenol remain dissolved in the ether layer while the salt of the carboxylic acid dissolves in the water layer. When solvent layers are separated, the neutral compound and the phenol remain in the organic layer. Further treatment of the organic layer with aqueous NaOH converts the phenol to its water soluble salt which can then be separated from the neutral compound which still remains in the organic layer. The neutral component can be recovered by simply evaporating the organic solvent. The carboxylic acid and phebol are then recovered by adding strong mineral acid such as Hcl to their respective aqueous layers. The strong acid converts the salts to molecular, (water-insoluble) weak carboxylic acid or phenol:

$$H^+ + RCOONa = RCOOH + Na^+$$

$$H^+ + ArONa = ArOH + Na^+$$

This experiment involves the separation of a neutral substance, a phenolic compound and a carboxylic acid from a mixture containing all three.

PROCEDURE

NOTE: The mixture for extraction contains equal parts of benzoic acid, 2-naphthol and 1,4-dichlorobenzene.

PART A: INITIAL SEPARATION

1. Place 0.500g of the mixture in 3mL of ether in a separatory funnel. Stopper the funnel and gently shake to dissolve the mixture. Remove the stopper frequently between shakes to relieve the pressure caused by the extremely volatile ether.
2. Once dissolution is complete, add 1-mL of 10% aqueous $NaHCO_3$. Stopper and shake to mix. Two layers should be observed. Allow the layers to separate then transfer the lower aqueous layer into a normal sized (NOT MICROSCALE) test tube labeled #2. Set this tube aside and go on to the next step of the extraction.
3. To the upper layer which remained in the separatory funnel, add 1-mL of 5% aqueous NaOH. Stopper and shake. Again two layers should be observed. Transfer the lower aqueous layer into another test tube labeled #3.
4. Transfer the remaining organic layer from the separatory funnel into a third test tube labeled #1.

PART B: RECRYSTALLIZATION AND RECOVERY OF COMPONENTS

1. To test tube #1 add anhydrous Na_2SO_4 until this solid drying agent no longer clumps. Stopper and let it sit for about ten minutes. Decant the entire solution unto a previously tared watch glass. Place the watch glass with the solution in the back of the hood and allow the ether to evaporate. Record the weight of the solid 1,4 dichlorobenzene recovered.

2. IN THE HOOD, cautiously add concentrated Hcl drop by drop to the contents of tube f2 until a permanent precipitate forms. Cool and then suction filter the precipitated crystals through a Hirsch funnel. Wash the crystals with cold deionized water. Press dry and record the weight if the benzoic acid recovered. Repeat this procedure with the contents of tube #3 and record the weight of the 2-naphthol recovered.

3. Calculate the percent recovery and obtain a melting range for each of the components. Record these values on your data sheet.

EXPERIMENT 5: Report and Worksheet

EXTRACTION

Student Name: _____   Day: _____

Student Number: _____   Date: _____

Mixture Components:

    (1)   ArCOOH, benzoic acid . . .MP: 123°C . . . pKa: 4.17
    (2)   ArOH, 2-naphthol . . . . .MP: 123°C . . . pKa: 9.51
    (3)   ArCl, p-dichlorobenzene .MP: 53°C

DATA

Mass of mixture used . . . . . _____ mg

TUBE 1: P-DICHLOROBENZENE	
mass recovered: mg	M.P. range: °C
% recovery:	

TUBE 2: BENZOIC ACID	
mass recovered: mg	M.P. range: °C
% recovery:	

TUBE 3: 2-NAPHTHOL	
mass recovered: mg	M.P. range: °C
% recovery:	

35

EXTRACTION FLOW CHART

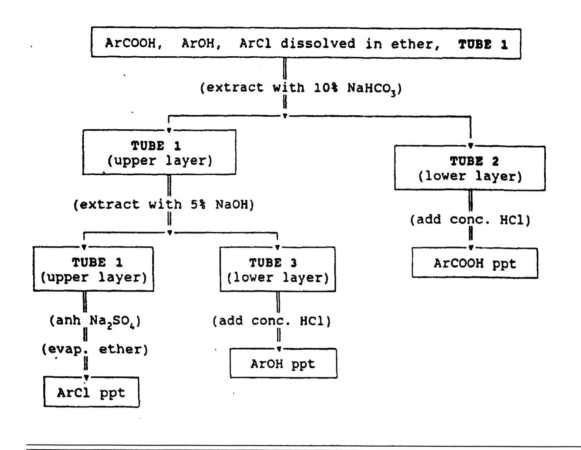

QUESTIONS

1) When draining liquid from a separatory funnel, WHY is it necessary to remove the stopper?

2) What is the equation for each of the following reactions?

    a) Benzoic acid + $NaHCO_3$

    b) Sodium benzoate + Hcl

    c) 2-Naphthol + NaOH

    d) Sodium naphtholate + Hcl

3) K_D **for "A" = C (ligroin) / C (water)   = 8.0**

a) What weight of "A" can be removed from a solution that contains 6.00 grams of "A" in 50.0-mLs of water by a SINGLE EXTRACTION using 50.0-mLs of ligroin?

b) What weight of "A" can be removed in TWO SUCCESSIVE EXTRACTIONS using 25.0-mLs of ligroin in each? (Assume 6.00 g of "A" is dissolved in 50.0-mLs of water.)

c) What volume of ligroin is needed to remove 99% of "A" in a single extraction? (Assume 6.00 g of "A" is dissolved in 50.0-mLs of water.)

d) Which is more effective, SIMPLE (as in part A) or MULTIPLE (as in part B) EXTRACTION?

CRYSTALLIZATION

PART A: SELECTION OF A RECRYSTALLIZING SOLVENT

Organic compounds as a whole follow the rule of thumb "like dissolves like" with respect to solubility. Thus nonpolar compounds dissolve in nonpolar solvents by molecular mixing, while polar compounds dissolve in polar solvents by a combination of molecular mixing and dipole-dipole attractions. Any polar compound which forms intermolecular hydrogen-bridge bonds is classified as "associated". Associated compounds dissolve in very polar associated solvents such as water by intermolecular hydrogen-bridge bonding or coassociation. Ionic compounds tend to dissolve in water by the same process in the formation of ion-dipole bonds. A large number of such ion-dipole bonds and the increased randomness of the solution state tend to overcome the strength of crystal lattice attractions in the solid state.

The process of dissolution usually involves physical rather than chemical changes. Usually, it signifies readjustment of intermolecular forces with no alteration of the essential intramolecular structures.

When an organic compound contains only hydrogen and carbon (a hydrocarbon), the molecule is essentially nonpolar. It will be soluble to a greater or lesser degree in nonpolar or slightly polar organic solvents such as ligroin (petroleum ether), benzene, toluene, ethyl ether, or carbon tetrachloride. In most cases, this solubility will increase as temperature increases because of the greater amount of kinetic energy available to bring about molecular mixing.

If an organic molecule contains, in addition to the hydrocarbon portion, one or more atoms of any electronegative element, the molecule is generally polar (unless a given structure .has the effect of canceling dipoles). The three most electronegative elements are N, 0, and F. Many organic molecules which contain one or more of these very electronegative atoms are capable of intermolecular association or hydrogen-bridge bonding, as is the case with alcohols (ROH) , carboxylic acids (RCOOH), amines (RNH$_2$) , and other common functional groups. Other organic molecules containing N, 0, or F such as ethers (ROR) , esters (RCOOR'), and carbonyl compounds (RCOR'), may be incapable of coassociation because they lack a hydrogen atom bonded directly to the electronegative element. In either case, each molecule contains a polar portion in the region of the functional group and a nonpolar portion in the region of the hydrocarbon. The polar portion is capable of forming hydrogen-bridge bonds with water and enhances the molecules solubility in water. The hydrocarbon portion is not water soluble but tends to dissolve in slightly polar or nonpolar solvents. As a result of these solubility differences, the observed solubility of a given molecule is a balance between the relative proportion of the part of the molecule which is polar and water-soluble and that which is nonpolar and insoluble in water.

All small organic molecules containing nitrogen, oxygen or fluorine are water-soluble and soluble in polar solvents. As the size of the hydrocarbon portion of the molecule increases, solubility in water decreases, with the borderline at about four or five carbon atoms per atom of oxygen, nitrogen or fluorine. As the hydrocarbon portion of a molecule increases, its solubility becomes essentially that of a pure hydrocarbon.

PROCEDURE

In this experiment, the solubilities of several organic compounds will be determined. Where possible, an appropriate recrystallizing solvent or solvent mixture will be selected. Solubility will be related to the structure of each solute-solvent pair.

THE SOLUTES WHOSE SOLUBILITY WILL BE TESTED ARE:
(1) benzoic acid
(2) resorcinol
(3) naphthalene

THE SOLVENTS WHICH WILL BE USED ARE:
(1) water
(2) toluene
(3) cyclohexane

A solute is classified as soluble when three or more grams dissolve per 100-mLs of the solvent. A proportional amount of each solute and solvent will be used. If a solute dissolves in cold solvent, it is classified as soluble. If the solute is insoluble or only partially soluble in cold solvent, its solubility will be tested in hot solvent. A good recrystallizing solvent must have a high temperature coefficient toward the solute, i.e. there must be a considerable difference between the solubility of the solute in hot as opposed to cold solvent.

```
******************************************************************
*CAUTION! Particular care must be taken in using toluene.  It is*
*quite flammable and has a very low boiling point.  It must be  *
*used in the hood, and heated only in a boiling water bath or   *
*electric sand bath, never with an open burner or flame.        *
******************************************************************
```

    1. Weigh out a 0.3-gram sample of one of the solutes. Divide this solid into three approximately equal volumes. Place each volume in a separate, clean, dry test tube. Label the test tubes 1,2, and 3.
    2. To the contents of tube number 1, add 3-mL of water. Stopper the tube and shake for one minute. Observe and record the observations in the appropriate section of your data sheet. Use the classifications:
             I...(insoluble)...no solute dissolved.
             P...(partly soluble)..some solute dissolved.
             S...(soluble)...all of the solute dissolved.
Observations must be clearly reported. Complete solubility indicates a uniform clear solution. The solution may not be cloudy, nor may it contain a separate liquid layer. Both these observations indicate insolubility or partial insolubility.
    3. If the solute is soluble in cold solvent, no further

testing is needed. If, however, the solute is insoluble or partially soluble in the cold solvent, then heat this test tube gently (STOPPER REMOVED) in a sand bath or hot water bath set up IN THE HOOD.

4. Agitate the contents of the tube with a stirring rod. Remove from the heat source and observe immediately, recording your observations. If the solute dissolved partially or completely, set the tube aside to see if recrystallization, occurs upon cooling. Record this observation in the appropriate place on the data sheet.

5. Repeat steps 1 through 4 with the solute in tube 2, using cyclohexane as the solvent instead of water.

6. Repeat steps 1 through 4 with the solute in tube 3 using toluene as the solvent.

7. For any solute which is soluble in toluene, add cyclohexane drop by drop to the solution and observe if any recrystallization occurs in the resulting solvent mixture. If no recrystallization occurs by the time an equal volume of cyclohexane has been added, then you may conclude that the solute is completely soluble in this solvent mixture as well. Record your results in the appropriate column of your data sheet.

8. Repeat all the above steps with the remainder of the solutes to be tested.

PART B: RECRYSTALLIZATION

Many crystalline organic solids are purified by a process termed crystallization or recrystallization. This makes use of the fact that a specific solvent shows a high temperature coefficient toward a given solute, while impurities may (1) remain completely insoluble in the solvent at all temperatures, or (2) remain completely soluble in the solvent at all temperatures. Limited purification can be achieved when both the solute and the impurities which contaminate it exhibit identical solubility characteristics toward the solvent used.

When a solvent shows a high temperature coefficient toward a solute, it dissolves the solute to a much greater extent in a hot solution than in a cold solution. An example of an appropriate solute-solvent pair for effective recrystallization is the benzoic acid-water system. The following solubilities are observed in grams of benzoic acid per 100-mL of water:

1.	0.21g of benzoic acid per 100-mL water at 10.0°C
2.	0.30g of benzoic acid per 100-mL water at 20.0°C
3.	2.75g of benzoic acid per 100-mL water at 80.0°C
4.	6.80g of benzoic acid per 100-mL water at 95.0°C

A graphical representation of the solubility versus temperature data for this solute-solvent pair is given below.

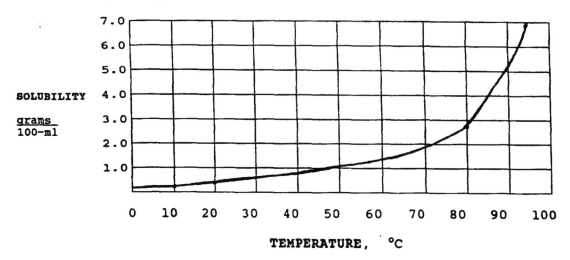

If 5.00 grams of benzoic acid is dissolved in water at 95°C, the volume of water required is:

$$5.00g \text{ benzoic acid} \times \frac{100\text{-mL water}}{6.80g \text{ acid}} = 73.5mL$$

When this solution is cooled to 10.0°C, the solubility of the benzoic acid decreases markedly, causing excess acid to crystallize and leaving a solution saturated with benzoic acid at the lower temperature. Thus at 10.0°c,

$$73.5mL \text{ water} \times \frac{0.21g \text{ acid}}{100\text{-mL water}} = 0.15g \text{ acid in solution}$$

This points out one of the inherent problems in the process of recrystallization. The maximum amount of benzoic acid that can be recovered is 5.00 grams - 0.15 grams, or 4.85 grams. Some loss of solute always occurs because of its solubility in the cold solvent. This loss becomes important when too much hot solvent is used initially to dissolve the solute. If 150-mL of solvent at 95°C were used to dissolve the 5.00 grams of benzoic acid, then 0.31 grams of the acid would remain dissolved in the cold water at 10.0°C.

HOW ARE IMPURITIES PRESENT IN THE ORIGINAL CRYSTALS REMOVED BY THE PROCESS OF RECRYSTALLIZATION?

1. **Impurities that are <u>insoluble at all temperatures</u>:** When the impure crystals are dissolved in the hot solvent, the impurities remain as undissolved solid particles. As long as .the solution remains hot, the crystals are dissolved (liquid state) but the impurities are undissolved (solid state). As the solution cools, the pure solute crystals begin to crystallize, again mixing with the solid impurities present. Therefore, separation must occur while the solution remains

hot. A simple filtration is performed on the hot solution. Since cooling brings about undesired recrystallization of the solute, the filtration of the hot solution is performed using a hot funnel. After hot filtration, the filtrate (liquid) may be cooled to recrystallize pure solute. The filtered impurities are discarded.

2. **Impurities that are <u>soluble in hot and cold solvent</u>:** When the impure solute is dissolved in hot solvent, the impurities also dissolve. As the solution cools, pure solute begins to crystallize since it is less soluble in the cold solvent. The impurities remain dissolved because they are soluble at all temperatures in the solvent. This presents one of the simplest methods of purifying crystalline solids.

3. **Impurities having the <u>same solubility as the solute</u>:** If the impure solute is dissolved in a hot solvent, any impurities having the same solubility characteristics also dissolve. As the solution is cooled, both begin to precipitate. This seems to indicate that no purification occurs. However, if the impurity is present in a relatively small amount, complete purification of the solute crystals is possible in one recrystallization step.

Suppose 6.8 grams of benzoic acid is contaminated with 0.20 grains of an impurity with similar solubility characteristics in water. When the mixture is dissolved in 100-mL of water at 95°C (remember solubilities are not mutually exclusive: both solutes are equally soluble in the same volume of water) and recrystallized at 10°C. 0.21 grams of the benzoic acid remain dissolved in the cold water along with 0.20 grams (ALL) of the soluble impurity. Thus, one recrystallization yields 6.6 grams of pure benzoic acid and NO IMPURITY.

Suppose a mixture is known to contain 6.8 grams of benzoic acid and 0.63 grams of an impurity having the same solubility as the benzoic acid. Then the mixture would be soluble in 100-mL of water at 95°C. However, recrystallization at 10°C would yield 6.6 grams of benzoic acid and 0.42 grams of the impurity. (Why?) Therefore, the minimum amount of water required to dissolve ALL of the impurity at the recrystallization temperature is:

$$\text{0.63g of impurity} \times \frac{\text{100-mL of water}}{\text{0.21g impurity}} = \text{300mL of water}$$

If this mixture is dissolved in 300-mL of water at 95°C and recrystallized at 10°C, 0.63 grams of benzoic acid remains dissolved and ALL of the impurity (0.63 grains) also remains dissolved. The recovery of pure benzoic acid is reduced to 6.2 grams. As the fraction of impurity having the same solubility as the solute increases, the yield of pure solute decreases. At some point, recrystallization of the solute using this particular solvent is no longer feasible because of the low yields of pure crystals. A new solvent or solvent system must be selected or a different method of purification must be used.

Simple recrystallization can be used effectively to eliminate impurities which are in the solvent, those which are completely soluble in the solvent, and, to a limited extent, those impurities which have the same solubility as the crystals being purified.

DECOLORIZATION

Sometimes high-molecular-weight by-products form during the process of a chemical reaction. These would often cause discoloration of usually clear or pale organic compounds and should be removed before crystallization is complete. This decolorization can be achieved by simply boiling the organic liquid with small pellets of activated charcoal.

Activated charcoal can bind many molecules of an impurity to itself since it has an extremely large surface area per gram. A finely divided powder would have an even larger surface area per gram, but the pelletized form is used instead since it is much easier to filter and separate from the organic liquid once decolorization is complete.

The only difficulty of this process is in determining just how much of the charcoal pellets should be used. If too little is added, then the solution will not decolorize completely, and if too much is added, then some of the desired product may be absorbed by the charcoal in addition to the colored impurities. Thus, some amount of trial and error might be necessary. A good beginning point would be to add approximately 10-20 pellets. If, on boiling, decolorization does not appear to be complete, then continue to add a couple of pellets at a time and reheat until the desired result is achieved. Any additional pellets should be added with extreme care and only once the liquid has been allowed to cool slightly. Charcoal pellets act in very much the same way as boiling chips do and may cause already hot liquids to superheat and boil over.

PROCEDURE

1. CRYSTALLIZATION OF PURE BENZOIC ACID: Weigh out approximately 150mg (0.150g) of benzoic acid in a 5-mL Erlenmeyer flask. Add an appropriate volume of water to dissolve the acid based on the solubility data given in the theory section. Add about a 20-50% excess of water to allow for any evaporation which may occur during heating. A useful guide for actually measuring the volume of water added would be that 1-mL is approximately equal to 25 drops delivered from the plastic disposable pipette.

Heat the solution gently on a sand bath until it almost boils. Maintain this temperature until all of the benzoic acid dissolves. If the solution actually boils, then some of the benzoic acid may be deposited on the sides of the Erlenmeyer flask. This would affect the percent recovery of the solute, so boiling should be avoided. If, after heating for some time, some of the benzoic acid still does not dissolve, add water a drop at a time until all the solute disappears.

Once dissolution is complete, allow the solution to cool to room temperature, observing the recrystallization as it takes place. After it reaches room temperature, cool further in a beaker of ice. Decant the water and transfer the crystals to a sheet of filter paper. Press dry as much as possible, weigh and record the melting range. Calculate the percent recovery of the product. Record your results on the data sheet.

2. DECOLORIZATION OF A SOLUTION: Place approximately 1-mL of a solution of methylene blue dye in a reaction tube. Add about ten pellets of activated charcoal. Shake and observe if there is any change to the color of the solution. Heat to boiling on a hot sand bath. If the solution does not discolor completely then cool it in a beaker of tap water, add a few more charcoal pellets and boil again. Record your observations of the color change and note how rapidly decolorization takes place.

EXPERIMENT 6: Report and Worksheet

PART A: SELECTION OF A RECRYSTALLIZING SOLVENT

Student Name: _____   Day: _____

Student Number: _____   Date: _____

_____

DATA

SOLVENTS	SOLIDS		
	NAPHTHALENE	BENZOIC ACID	RESORCINOL
WATER:			
COLD			
HOT			
RECRYS.			
CYCLOHEXANE:			
COLD			
HOT			
RECRYS.			
TOLUENE:			
COLD			
HOT			
RECRYS.			
TOLUENE + CYCLOHEXANE MIXTURE:			
RECRYS.			

Part B: RECRYSTALLIZATION

Student Name: _____   Day: _____

Student Number: _____   Date: _____

DATA

1. **CRYSTALLIZATION OF BENZOIC ACID**

    mass of benzoic acid used ...... _____ mg

    mass of benzoic acid recovered .... _____ nig

    melting range (ref. HP 122°C) . .... _____ °C

    $$\textbf{PERCENT RECOVERY} = \frac{\textbf{mass recovered}}{\textbf{mass initial}} \times 10^2 = \underline{\hspace{2cm}} \%$$

CALCULATIONS:

(A) Volume of 95'C water needed to dissolve benzoic acid

(B) Mass of benzoic acid that can be removed at 10'C

2. **DECOLORIZING METHYLENE BLUE SOLUTION OBSERVATIONS:**

    _____

    _____

    _____

QUESTIONS

1. For each solute tested in PART A, which solvent is the BEST CHOICE for recrystallization? Explain your choice.

2. What are the steps for crystallization?

3. What VOLUME (mLs) of 95° water is needed to dissolve 10 grams of benzoic acid? (Use solubility data in text).

   (A) If this solution is cooled to 10°C and recrystallized, how many GRAMS of benzoic acid will crystalize?

   (B) What is the maximum percent recovery?

4. How is activated carbon used in the recrystallizing process? Why should a large excess of activated carbon be avoided?

5. Under what circumstances is a miscible solvent mixture more effective than a single solvent in the recrystallization process?

THEORY SUBLIMATION

Sublimation is defined as the change from the solid state to the gaseous state without passing through an intermediate liquid state. Numerous solids are capable of being sublimed at elevated temperatures and/or reduced pressures. The only requirement is that the solid must have a slight vapor pressure under the applied conditions.

Sublimation may be used as a purification technique. Any solid substance which can be sublimed may be separated from nonvolatile contaminants by sublimation. The mixture is usually warmed to bring about the vaporization of the subliming solid. Other contaminants remain in the solid state. The vapor is then condensed on a cool surface ("cold finger") as purified solid.

This technique of purification is particularly useful for small amounts of solid. It is essentially a molecular distillation process.

In this experiment, an unknown to be purified by sublimation will be contaminated with nonvolatile impurities. A small portion of this solid will be sublimed and condensed. The identity of the unknown will be determined by its melting point.

PROCEDURE

1) Obtain unknown. Place a moderate quantity of the unknown across the bottom of the 50-mL filter flask.

2) Place a rubber pipet bulb over the side-arm of this flask. This allows for some increase in pressure due to heating without loss or contamination of material.

3) Using the neorene adapter and a centrifuge tube, close the top of the filter flask. Allow the centrifuge tube to dip into the filter flask to a 1/4 inch above the solid.

4) Fill the centrifuge tube with ice and water. This serves as the "cold finger" condenser. Sublimed solid will condense on its surface.

5) Clamp the entire assembly carefully on a sand bath and begin to warm.

6) Remove the assembly from heat when sufficient solid has condensed on the cold finger.

7) Before opening the assembly, use a plastic disposable pipet to remove the ice-water. Replace it with room temperature water. This prevents water vapor from condensing on the just-sublimed solid.

8) Carefully remove the centrifuge tube. Scrape the sublimed solid off the tube and obtain a melting point.

SUBLIMATION APPARATUS:

1....CENTRIFUGE TUBE
2....NEOPRENE ADAPTER
3....25-mL FILTER FLASK
4....PIPET BULB
5....SUBLIMATE
6....MATERIAL TO BE
     SUBLIMED

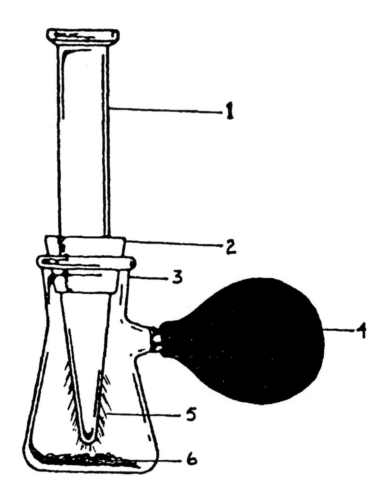

Sublimation Unknowns

Compound	Melting Point °C
1,4-dichlorobenzene	55
naphthalene	82
1-naphthol	96
acetanilide	114
benzoic acid	122
salicylic acid	159
camphor	177
caffeine	235

Organic Chemistry Experiments Laboratory Manuals (CHM 2210L and 2211L)

EXPERIMENT 7: Report and Worksheet

SUBLIMATION

Student Name: _____   Day: _____

Student Number: _____   Date: _____

_____

DATA

1. SUBLIMATION OF ACETANILIDE (MP = 114-C)

MP range of impure acetanilide. .... _____ °C

MP range of sublimed acetanilide... _____ °C

2. UNKNOWN NUMBER _____

Appearance of unknown before sublimation:

MP range of unknown before sublimation .. _____ °C

MP range of unknown after sublimation ... _____ °C

IDENTITY OF UNKNOWN : _____

_____

QUESTIONS

1. Define SUBLIMATION.

51

2. What characteristics must a compound possess to be effectively purified by sublimation ?

STEAM DISTILLATION

Introduction

Steam distillation is a method used to separate slightly volatile solids or liquids from nonvolatile materials. It differs from ordinary distillation in several ways. The solid or liquid to be distilled must be immiscible in water creating a two-phase system for the distillation. The distilled substance must show a slight vapor pressure, as little as five or ten mm being sufficient, at elevated temperatures. Steam distillation proceeds at some constant temperature below 100'C. as long as water and the distilling phase are present. In addition, the distillate consists of two phases, water and the distilled solid or liquid. The two phases distil in a constant proportion and they are miscible only in the gaseous state.

Steam distillation is the preferred method for separation when the substance to be separated (1) decomposes at its usual boiling point or at high temperature, (2) occurs mixed with large quantities of tarry materials, or (3) exists as an intramolecular hydrogen-bonding isomer mixed with isomers that hydrogen-bond intennolecularly. Steam distillation is used to remove caffeine from coffee and from other food products.

When two immiscible phases are heated for distillation, each phase exerts its own vapor pressure. The vapor pressure of each phase depends only on the temperature, not on the quantity or the nature of the other phase. Thus, when a slightly volatile water-insoluble liquid "X" is steam distilled with water, the "X" exerts its own vapor pressure at each higher temperature, and the water also exerts its own vapor pressure at each higher temperature. The table below shows the vapor pressures of "X" and water at several temperatures:

Temperature, °C	20	35	50	90	95	100
Water, mm Hg	17	42	93	530	634	760
"X", mm Hg	5	25	60	230	390	520

Observe that at 90°C, the sum of the vapor pressures of "X" and water equals 76 mm Hg. At this temperature, the mixture will begin to distil. In the gaseous state, the sum of the pressures of water and "X" represents the total pressure of the system. The partial pressure of "X" at the distillation temperature is proportional to the number of molecules of "X" being distilled:

$$p_X \propto N_X \quad \text{and} \quad p_{WATER} \propto N_{WATER}$$

where p is the partial pressure, and N represents the number of moles and is proportional to the number of molecules of each substance present. Since the distillation proceeds at a constant temperature, the ratio p_X/p_{WATER} is also constant. This indicates that the molar ratio N_X/N_{WATER} is constant as well:

$$\frac{p_x}{p_{WATER}} \quad = \quad \frac{N_x}{N_{WATER}} \quad = \quad constant$$

In spite of the fact that substance "X" has a much lower vapor pressure than water at the distillation temperature, its steam distills at a favorable weight ratio. To understand how this is possible, it must be remembered that this distillation proceeds at a constant mole ratio, with "X" being distilled much more slowly than water. However, the Molar Mass of water is 18 grams, while that of most organic compounds is 100 grains or more. The "X" in this example has a Molar Mass of 90 grams. Since the vapor pressure of each' substance is proportional to its number of moles, vapor pressure x Molar Mass is proportional to the mass of the substance being distilled:

$$constant \quad = \quad \frac{(p_x) \ (Molar \ Mass_x)}{(p_{WATER}) \ (Molar \ Mass_{WATER})}$$

In this example, the theoretical weight ratio obtained during the distillation of "X" is calculated as follows:

$$constant = \frac{(230 \ mm)(90 \ g/mol)}{(530 \ mm)(18 \ g/mol)} = \frac{2.2}{1.0} = 2.2$$

Calculations show that 2.2 grams of "X" will distill over every time 1.0 gram of water is distilled. Although there exists an unfavorable mole ratio for this distillation, the mass ratio favors "X" because of the very low Molar Mass of water. Recall that the components, although miscible in the gaseous state, again separate into two phases when condensed.

To obtain the theoretical weight ratio for a given steam distillation, the vapor pressures of both the organic phase and the water must be known for the temperature range between 70°C and 100°C. That temperature at which the $P_{ORG} + P_{UATER} = 760$ mm represents the distillation temperature and the proper ratio of vapor pressures. Often the theoretical weight ratio is difficult to determine because of the lack of availability of vapor pressure data about the organic component being distilled.

To calculate the experimental weight ratio for a given distillation is quite simple. Once the steam distillation has proceeded for a period of, time, the distillate (consisting of the organic phase and water) is measured^ The volume of water collected multiplied by its density represents the mass of water distilled. The volume of the organic phase (if liquid) times its density represents the mass of the organic phase collected. Thus,

$$constant \ weight \ ratio \quad = \quad \frac{(V_{ORGANIC}) \ (D_{ORGANIC})}{(V_{WATER}) \ (D_{WATER})}$$

If the organic phase is a solid, it is weighed and this weight is compared to the weight of water distilled.

Experimental results obtained in steam distillation often differ slightly from theoretical predictions. The error lies in assuming that the organic phase and the water phase remain completely immiscible at elevated temperatures. As miscibility increases, the vapor pressures are altered (altering the ratio) and the two phases are no longer completely independent of each other.

In this experiment, a mixture of p-dichlorobenzene (M.P.= 53'C) and salicylic acid
(M.P. = 158°C) will be separated by steam distillation. Each compound will be recovered quantitatively and tested for purity. The p-dichlorobenzene is a solid which exhibits a slight vapor pressure and can be steam distilled. The salicylic acid shows essentially zero vapor pressure and cannot be steam distilled.

In addition, a mixture of bromobenzene and water will be steam distilled and the weight ratio for this distillation will be determined.

PROCEDURE

This experiment is best performed by a group of two students working together. While one student arranges the steam distillation apparatus in the HOOD. the second, student begins the steps outlined in PART I.

Apparatus for Steam Distillation:
1 Steam Generator: filled 1/2 to 2/3 with tapwater and boiling chips.
2 Safety Tube: an approximately 3-foot long glass tube; placed below the water level...a high level of water in this tube indicates blockage somewhere in the steam line, and the safety trap must be opened.
3 Safety Trap: to be opened when water condenses in line to relieve pressure buildup.
4 Distilling Flask: contains the material to be steam distilled ...steam inlet tube should be below the liquid level.
5 Condenser
6 Curved (Vacuum) Adapter: secured by a rubber band.
7 Receiver: should be cooled by an ice-water bath.

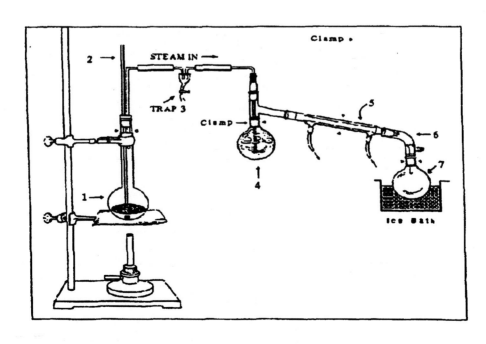

PART I. Steam Distillation of a Mixture of p-Dichlorobenzene and Salicylic Acid.

1. Weigh out 2.0 grams of p-dichlorobenzene and 4.0 grams of salicylic' acid.
2. Mix well using a mortar and pestle if needed.
3. Measure and record the melting range of a capillary sample of this mixture.
4. After the distillation apparatus has been assembled and checked by the instructor, remove the distilling flask, and begin heating the steam generator using the Bunsen burner.
5. By use of a powder funnel, transfer the mixture of solids to the distilling flask. Be sure to hold the flask in such a way that no solid is lost through the side-arm.
6. Add approximately 40-mL of distilled water, washing down any solid clinging to the neck of the flask.
7. Reconnect the distilling flask to the steam generator, leaving the safety trap open.
8. . As soon as the water in the steam generator boils, close the safety trap and run a gentle stream of water through the condenser. Set a 150-mL beaker in an ice bath as the receiver.
9. Steam distil at a vigorous rate using additional heating on the distilling flask as needed (this involves a second Bunsen burner).
10. As the p-dichlorobenzene distills and condenses, a white haze or a clump of white solid will be observed in the condenser. When this happens, water to the condenser should be turned off temporarily in order to allow the solid to pass into the receiver. If the water is left off too long, there will be insufficient cooling and a large quantity of the p-dichlorobenzene will be lost by evaporation. Thus, the water to the condenser must be turned on and off as needed.
11. Continue in this manner until NO white haze or solid forms in the condenser with water running. Steam distil for an additional five minutes.
12. Open the safety trap and discontinue heating.

NOTE: While one student continues with the filtering, drying, and measurements outlined in this steam distillation, the second student should perform Part II- the steam distillation of bromobenzene.

13. Salicylic acid dissolved in hot water remains in the distilling flask. Using asbestos or ceramic gloves, remove the digtilling flask and immediately pour the hot liquid into a clear 250-mL beaker. Allow to cool slightly and then place in an ice-water bath. This will effect the recrystallization of salicylic acid.
14. To the cold solution of salicylic acid, add 5-mL of concentrated HCl. This will increase the amount of precipitated acid because addition of H_3O^* shifts any weak acid equilibrium to the formation of more un-ionized acid.
15. Suction filter the salicylic acid crystals, washing with two 5-mL portions of distilled water while on the suction funnel.
16. Press dry and weigh the crystals of salicylic acid. Determine the melting range. Record all data.
17. Separate the crystals of p-dichlorobenzene from the water in the 150-mL receiver by simple filtration using the glass funnel and filter paper.
18. Press-dry the crystals of p-dichlorobenzene using a pestle if needed to crush them.

19. Weigh and obtain the melting range of the p-dichlorobenzene. Record on the data sheet.

Part II. Steam Distillation of Bromobenzene

1. To the CLEAN distilling flask, add 44-mL of bromobenzene and 40-mL of distilled water.

2. Reconnect to the steam generator, using a 25-mL Graduated cylinder as the receiver.

3. Steam distil rapidly until a volume of 25 mLs of total distillate has been collected. Set aside the collected product, and replace the receiver by another 25-mL Graduated cylinder.

4. Continue rapid steam distillation until a second volume of 25 mLs of total distillate has been collected. Set the receiver aside.

5. Disconnect the apparatus and clean out the distilling flask thoroughly. Boiling chips must be discarded in the waste bin.

6. Measure the volume of water and the volume of bromobenzene present in each 25-mL Graduated cylinder. Record. The bromobenzene has a density of 1.5 g/mL and will be the lower layer in each case.

<u>EXPERIMENT 8: Report and Worksheet</u>

STEAM DISTILLATION

Student Name: _____   Day: _____

Student Number: _____   Date: _____

DATA

I. Steam Distillation of a Mixture of p-Dichlorobenzene and Salicylic Acid

melting range of original mixture....   _____

grams of salicylic acid used.........   _____

grams of salicylic acid recovered....   _____

% recovery of salicylic acid.........   _____

melting range of salicylic acid......   _____

grams of p-dichlorobenzene used....   _____

grams of p-dichlorobenzene recovered. _____

% recovery of p-dichlorobenzene......   _____

melting range of p-dichlorobenzene...   _____

II. Steam Distillation of Bromobenzene

Bromobenzene (lower).... _____ mLs ... _____ g (#1)

_____ mLs ... _____ g (#2)

Water (upper) .... _____mLs ... _____g (#1)

_____ mLs . . . _____ g (# 2)

Ratio (lower)/(upper)   Sample #1 _____   Sample #2 _____

QUESTIONS

1. Using experimental data obtained in this lab, describe the effectiveness of steam distillation in the separation of a mixture of salicylic acid and p-dichlorobenzene.

2. The theoretical weight ratio for the steam distillation of bromobenzene is 1.6. How does your experimental value compare with this theoretical ratio? What might account for any differences?

3. A water-insoluble slightly volatile organic compound "M" steam distils at 98.5°C. At this temperature the vapor pressure of water is 747 nun Hg, and that of compound "M" is 13 mm Hg. If the Molar Mass of "M" is 130 grams, what is the theoretical weight ratio for the steam distillation of "M" at this temperature? What is the % by weight of "M" in this distillate?

4. Compare and contrast steam distillation with ordinary distillation with respect to:

(a) nature of materials being distilled

(b) composition of the vapor state during distillation, and

(c) temperature during distillation of the vapor.

PREPARATION OF CYCLOHEXENE

One of the most convenient methods to prepare an alkene is by the dehydration of an alcohol. The mechanism for this reaction is illustrated below:

(1) $\underset{H}{C}-C-O-H$ + HB = $\underset{H}{C}-C-\underset{H}{O}-H^+$ + :B⁻

(2) $\underset{H}{C}-C-\underset{H}{O}-H^+$ + :B⁻ = $\underset{H}{C}-C^+$ + H_2O

(3) $\underset{H}{C}-C^+$ + :B⁻ = -C=C- + H:B

A trace of strong mineral acid is required for the reaction. This serves to protonate the alcohol and form a better leaving group, Hg'O rather than OH'. A relatively high temperature is needed to form the less stable carbocations, thus most reaction mixtures are heated. Two acids commonly used for this purpose are concentrated sulfuric acid and concentrated phosphoric acid. Both are strong enough to bring about the reaction while remaining reasonably heat stable.

Once the carbocation has been formed, (step 2 of the mechanism), it may (a) rearrange to form a more stable carbocation, (b) add to a second molecule of an alcohol to form a protonated ether, or (c) eliminate a hydrogen ion to form an alkene.

```
        ┌─── ---rearrangement---->  -C-C⁺   ----►  alkenes and
        │                              H            addition products
        │
  -C-C⁺─┤─── ---elimination of H⁺---------------►   -C=C-
    H   │
        │
        └─── ---addition to ROH----------------►   C-C-O-C-C⁺
                                                    H   H
```

The formation of the alkene is NOT favored by equilibrium. However, since alkenes have lower boiling points than their parent alcohols, equilibrium can be shifted toward alkene formation simply by distilling the product alkene out of the reaction mixture as soon as it is formed. Ether formation is favored by the presence of large quantities of nonprotonated alcohol. Thus, when ether is the desired product, additional alcohol is added as the reaction is carried out.

To avoid a mixture of alkenes arising from the rearrangement of the carbocation, alcohols are selected whose structure ensures one major alkene product.

In summary, dehydration of alcohols is carried out under those conditions which favor maximum yields of the alkene and which minimize other competing reactions. After proper selection of the alcohol to be dehydrated, the first requirement is a sufficiently high temperature to produce carbocations. No additional alcohol is added during the reaction because it would increase the yield of ether in the product mixture. Furthermore, the temperature must be maintained above that needed for carbocation formation but below the boiling point of the parent alcohol. Whether the alkene or the ether is the desired product, continued distillation and product removal must be carried out.

In this experiment, the cyclic alcohol, cyclohexanol, will be dehydrated to form cyclohexene. (WHY IS ONLY ONE ALKENE FORMED?)

PROCEDURE

Place 2.0g of cyclohexanol and 0.5mL of 85% phosphoric acid in a 5-mL long-necked round-bottom flask. Add a boiling chip and LOOSELY pack the neck of the flask with copper sponge. Swirl the flask to mix the layers. The mixture should get hot.

Attach the flask to a sidearm connector using a neoprene adapter. Close the other end of the connector with a thermometer and thermometer adapter, making sure that the bulb of the thermometer is below the sidearm of the connector. Next, attach the sidearm of the connector to a water-jacketed condenser. Clamp the entire assembly with the flask resting in a sand bath. Carefully wrap the neck of the flask and the sidearm connector with an ice pack made from aluminum foil. Place a 2-dram vial resting in a 30-mL beaker ice bath at the other end of the condenser to receive the distillate.

Begin heating gently and continue to distill until most of the residue in the flask has boiled over and very little distillate is being formed. Remove the assembly from the sand bath and allow it to cool for a few minutes.

Remove the thermometer and introduce another 2.0g of cyclohexanol. Redistill as before until only a small volume of residue (approximately 0.5mL) remains. Allow the flask to cool once more.

Transfer the entire contents of the collecting vial to a 5-mL Erienmeyer flask. This should consist of the organic product and an aqueous layer. Wash the mixture with an equal volume of saturated sodium chloride solution. This "salting out" decreases the solubility of cyclohexene in water. Remove the aqueous layer.

Add anhydrous sodium sulfate to the contents of the flask until the solid no longer clumps together. Shake the solution with this drying agent and then let the product sit for at least 5 minutes. When clear, decant the liquid into a tared vial. Report your yield in grams and calculate your percent yield. Normally, at this stage of the procedure, yet another distillation might be performed to further purify the product. In most cases, however, this last step would not be necessary. As a check, run the product on the IR and/or the GC and interpret it for purity. In the IR spectrum, look for peaks due to the starting material. Since the boiling points of expected impurities differ markedly from that of the desired product, gas chromatography is especially useful in this analysis. Use your analysis to determine if redistillation is necessary.

APPARATUS FOR CYCLOHEXENE PREPARATION:

1....THERMOMETER
2....THERMOMETER ADAPTER
3....SIDEARM CONNECTOR
4....WATER OUTLET
5....WATER INLET
6....CONDENSER
7....COPPER SPONGE
8....5-ml LONG NECKED FLASK
9....SAND BATH
10...COLLECTING VIAL
11...30-mL BEAKER WITH ICE

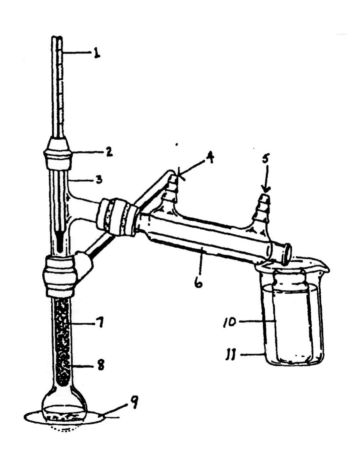

EXPERIMENT 9: Report and Worksheet

PREPARATION OF CYCLOHEXENE

Student Name: _____   Day: _____

Student Number: _____   Date: _____

_____

DATA

BALANCED EQUATION FOR REACTION:

Volume cyclohexanol used .... _____ mL _____ g _____ Moles

Grains of cyclohexene recovered .... _____ g

RI of cyclohexene .... _____ REF .... _____

THEORETICAL YIELD OF CYCLOHEXENE ...... _____ g
(show calculations)

PERCENT YIELD .... _____

"PURITY (GC): _____
(Instructor to fill out.)

_____

QUESTIONS

1. What is the MECHANISM for this preparation of cyclohexene ?

2. How is the yield of cyclohexene affected if the distillation receiver is allowed to warm up to room temperature?

3. WHY is the crude distillate mixed with an equal volume of saturated Nad ?

4. WHY is anhydrous sodium sulfate used in the purification?

EXPERIMENT 10

BUTENES FROM 2-BUTANOL

The dehydration of alcohols is conveniently carried out by heating the alcohol with a mineral acid. Sulfuric acid or phosphoric acid are generally used because each is strong enough to provide a proton and each is fairly stable to heating.

The mechanism for the dehydration of ethanol is indicated below. The SLOW STEP is reversible, but the formation of an alkene is favored by distilling out the alkene (lower BP) as it forms.

$$CH_3CH_2--OH \ + \ H+ \ ------------> \ CH_3CH_2--OH_2+$$

$$CH_3CH_2--OH_2+ \ ----(slow)------> \ CH_3CH_2+ \ + \ H_2O$$

$$CH_3CH_2+ \ -----(-H+)------> \ CH_2=CH_2$$

Since the reaction involves formation of carbocations, rearrangements may occur within the carbon skeleton. In addition, a mixture of alkenes is possible when more than one type of hydrogen may be eliminated.

When 2-butanol is heated with acid, it follows a mechanism similar to the one outlined above. The sec-butyl carbocation formed undergoes elimination of an adjacent proton to form the appropriate alkene.

$$\overset{+}{CH_3CH_2CHCH_3} \\ a b$$

(a) Elimination of a proton from "a" + will lead to the formation of 2-butene (both cis and trans)
(b) Elimination of a proton from "b" will lead to the formation of 1-butene.

The relative proportion of each product is related to the stability of the transition state producing it. The relative retention time of each product in GC analysis is dependent upon the polarity of each species.

PROCEDURE

1) Place about 15-20 drops of 2-butanol in a clean, dry reaction tube. Add 4 drops of cone. sulfuric acid while keeping the tube in an ice-water bath.

2) Insert a syringe needle through a rubber septum so that the syringe needle head is inside the reaction tube and the needle point sticks out when the septum is placed on the reaction tube.

3) Attach microscale polyethylene tubing to the exposed needle. Run this tubing into a water filled septum-capped 10-crn column. Cap the mouth with a finger and invert into a water bath (beaker). The butenes will be collected by downward displacement of water since they are not soluble in water.

4) Lower the reaction tube into a hot (100'C) sand bath. Increase the heat slowly to produce the reaction.

5) Collect several milliliters of the butene mixture.

6) Remove the tubing from the water bath and remove the reaction tube from the sand bath.

69

7) Cap the collection tube with another septum while it remains under water. Be sure that the product mixture does not escape.

8)Analyze the butene mixture on the Gas Chromatograph as directed by the instructor.

APPARATUS FOR BUTENE PREPARATION:

1....RUBBER SEPTUM
2....SYRINGE NEEDLE
3....REACTION TUBE
4....REACTION MIXTURE
5....SAND BATH
6....POLYETHYLENE TUBING
7....COLLECTION TUBE
8....LARGE BEAKER OF WATER

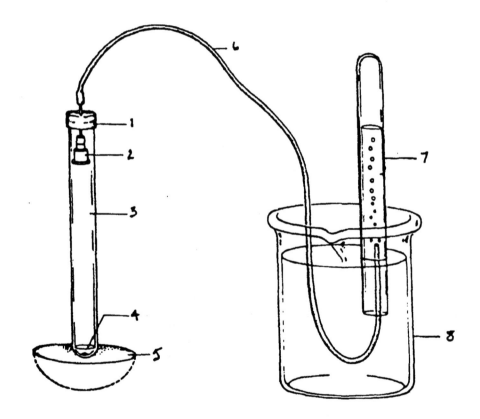

ANALYSIS BY GAS CHROMATOGRAPHY

Gas chromatography is one of the roost useful analytical tools available today. It is in principle similar to distillation, extraction, column chromatography and thin-layer chromatography. It is superior in many ways to these other techniques of separation. Gas chromatography can be used effectively on very small samples (10^{-3} to 10^{-15} grams). An efficient, properly selected column allows for the separation of compounds that have the same boiling point, similar polarities and similar masses.

A GAS CHROMATOGRAPH CONSISTS OF:

(1) A column (temperature controlled)
(2) An injection port (sample is volatilized)
(3) A detector (sensitive to material eluting from column)
(4) A moving phase (carrier gas such as He or N_2)
(5) A stationary phase (nonvolatile material in column)

The column with its support packing and its stationary phase is. thermostatically controlled at some desired temperature. Carrier gas is passed through the column at a steady flow rate. A sample of material to be separated is then injected by syringe at the injection port. This port is usually heated to some temperature high enough to volatilize the sample without decomposing it. The sample then mixes with the carrier gas and begins to pass through the column. In the column, the sample distributes between the stationary phase and the moving phase. This distribution is called adsorption if the stationary phase is a solid and the sample adsorbs on its surface. This type of gas chromatograph is called GSC, a gas-solid chromatograph. More commonly, the distribution is called partition, with the stationary phase being liquid and the sample dissolving in it. This type of gas chromatogram is called GLC, gas-liquid chromatography.

Once the sample is on the column, an equilibrium is established between dissolved sample and the sample in the carrier gas. The continuous flow of carrier gas causes constant equilibration as the sample is carried through the column. This is, in effect, creating hundreds of thousands of equilibria (theoretical plates) and causing a separation of each different component of the sample. The first component to reach the detector has the shortest retention time and has the least affinity for the stationary phase. Each component of the sample is eluted in its •turn, based directly on its retention time on the column and on its affinity for the stationary phase. The most useful rule is "like dissolves like".

Optimum operation is achieved when each component of a sample is well-separated from other components and each component gives its own retention time. Improper separation may yield peaks that overlap or peaks that are spread out too much. The proper operating conditions must be determined for each mixture to be separated. The selection of the stationary phase is most critical. There are many types of columns which have been developed. Each is most effective for its particular type of separation. Once the proper column is chosen, two other factors must be considered. One is the flow rate of the carrier gas. At high flow rates, the sample is rapidly moved through the column, thus decreasing the number of liquid-gas equilibria that can be achieved and therefore decreasing the efficiency of the column. If the flow rate is too low, the time required for the sample to clear the column is tremendously increased. Some middle value must be chosen for the carrier gas flow rate. The other adjustable factor which must be considered is the temperature of the column itself. A similar effect to that achieved by adjustment of the gas flow rate is observed here. If the temperature is raised too much, the retention time is considerably decreased for all components of a mixture since heating decreases the solubility of a gas in a liquid. If the temperature is too low, the retention time is increased for all components. The best separation is achieved as a compromise between rapid analysis and good separation.

The Perkin-Elmer Gas Chromatograph that will be used in this lab is equipped with a Flame Ionization Detector, FID, that gives an electrical response as a compound is eluted from the column. This type of detector DOES NOT give an equally intense response for equal molar quantities of different substances.

EXPERIMENT 10: Report and Worksheet

BUTENES FROM 2-BUTANOL GC ANALYSIS

Student Name: _____   Day: _____

Student Number: _____   Date: _____

DATA

GC ANALYSIS (ATTACH SPECTRUM)

Retention Time	Percent	Assigned Structure

QUESTIONS

1. What is the MECHANISM for this dehydration ?

2. What THREE alkenes are obtained from the dehydration of 2- BUTANOL ?

(A) Which of these is MOST POLAR ? LEAST POLAR ?

(B) Which of these has the HIGHEST BP ? LOWEST BP ?

3. What are the components of a gas chromatograph?

4. How are the compounds actually separated by gas chromatography?

5. How is retention time related to BP ? to POLARITY ?

6. How does each of the following affect the RETENTION TIME for gas chromatography ?

   (A) Increasing the carrier gas flow rate.

(B) Raising the column temperature.

7. If two peaks are closely spaced in a gas chromatograph, what will happen if:

(A) carrier gas flow rate is increased ?

(B) column temperature is increased ?

EXPERIMENT 11

ALKYNES: PREPARATION and PROPERTIES OF ACETYLENE

INTRODUCTION

Acetylene is the most important member of the alkyne family, it contains a carbon to carbon triple bond (with each carbon atom sp hybridized) which is responsible for many of its reactions. This triple bond accounts for the ease with which electrophilic addition occurs and for the oxidability of the alkyne. Acetylene also contains a slightly acidic carbon to hydrogen bond which allows certain acid-base reactions to occur.

At the turn of the century, acetylene was used in the headlamps of automobiles because of its luminous flame. Today, it is used in welding (the acetylene torch) and in organic synthesis.

In the laboratory, acetylene is conveniently prepared by the hydrolysis of calcium carbide, CaC_2, according to the equation:

$$CaC_2 \ + \ 2H_2O \ \text{---}\!\!> \ C_2H_2 \ + \ Ca(OH)_2$$

This equation represents one example of a Bronstead-Lowry acid-base reaction. When water is added to calcium carbide, an spontaneous reaction occurs, with acetylene gas being evolved. Water, a stronger acid than acetylene, transfers its proton to the acetylide ion, Ca^{-2}, to form the weaker acid C_2H_2 and the weaker base OH".

The acetylene gas produced in this fashion is collected by displacement of water because acetylene is insoluble in water. Acetylene is a poisonous, odorless gas. Any odor observed during its preparation is caused by impurities in the calcium carbide rather than by acetylene itself.

In this experiment, acetylene gas will be prepared by the action of water on calcium carbide and some of its numerous reactions will be studied.

PROCEDURE

CAUTION: PREPARATION AND TESTING OF ACETYLENE MUST BE DONE IN THE HOOD. EXCESS CALCIUM CARBIDE MUST BE REACTED IN THE HOOD. THIS WILL MINIMIZE EXCESS GAS ACCUMULATION SINCE ACETYLENE IS EXPLOSIVE IN AIR OVER A WIDE CONCENTRATION RANGE.

I. Preparation of Acetylene.

1. Fill a clean, dry 250 mL-RB flask to approximately 1/4 capacity with lump calcium carbide. No weighing of the calcium carbide is necessary. Arrange for the preparation and collection of acetylene as shown on the next page.

   (1) Separatory Funnel, containing about 30 mL of tapwater.
   (2) Claisen Adapter, one end to deliver tube.
   (3) 250-RB flask containing the lump calcium carbide.

(4) Rubber Piece of Thermometer Adapter, serving to secure the delivery tube.

(5) Gas-Collecting Bottles, filled with water and inverted in trough. A total of six such bottles will be needed.

(6) Trough, filled with water, with an overflow tube leading to a drain.

(7) Clamps, located to assure safety and ease of handling.

(8) Ice-Water Bath, used to cool the exothermic reaction.

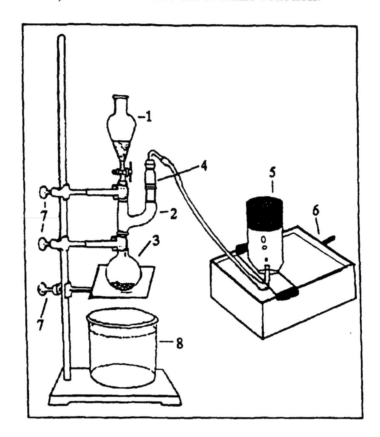

2. Before positioning the separatory funnel, fill the trough to approximately 2/3 capacity with tapwater. Be sure to attach overflow valve. Then. fill FIVE gas collecting bottles with tapwater. Cover, invert, and place in the trough.

3. Check the separatory funnel to make sure there are no stopcock leaks and that it can deliver one drop of water at a time. Attach to the assembly and fill with about 50 mL of water.

4. With CAUTION add one drop of water and collect the acetylene produced in one of the gas-collecting bottles. If too much water is added at once, all of the acetylene is produced at once. This may cause the fittings to come apart. Continue adding the water dropwise to maintain a moderate continual production of acetylene. If the reaction is interrupted for any length of time, temperature differences may cause the backup of water from the trough into the reaction flask. To prevent this, keep the gas-delivery tube above water level whenever an interruption occurs.

5. Continue in this fashion until the gas-collecting bottle is filled. Remove the filled bottle, covering with a glass square or watch glass lubricated with stopcock grease. Place it upright (still covered) in the back of the hood. Fill THREE (3) additional bottles in this way.

6. Bubble acetylene into the fifth bottle until it is about 1/20 filled. Then lift this bottle out of the water, upside down, allowing the water to drain out. Immediately cover it with a glass square. Label for use in the explosion reaction.

7. If the calcium carbide used was insufficient to fill all five bottles, fill a clean, dry 100 mL-RB flask to 1/3 capacity and quickly replace it for the 250 mL-RB flask assembly.

8. When all five gas-collecting bottles have been properly filled, set the stopcock of the separatory funnel to deliver water at a slow rate and push the assembly to the back of the hood. All unreacted calcium carbide must be destroyed and the acetylene removed through the hoods.

9. Decant most of the liquid in the 250 mL-RB flask down the sink located in the hood. Pour the remaining slurry of calcium hydroxide and water into an appropriately labeled container. Calcium hydroxide will clog the drain if it is discarded there.

II. Reactions of Acetylene.

1 Flammability. This must be done in the hood, with the window down as far as possible for safety.
   (a) Ignite a wood splint making sure that it is burning.
   (b) Hold the burning splint next to the mouth of a filled acetylene bottle.
   (c) Remove the glass square and immediately ignite. Take care to keep your hands well away from the reaction.
   (d) Observe and record the appearance of the flame.
   (e) Using a 250 mL beaker containing some tapwater, pour the water down the side into the burning acetylene bottle.
   (f) Note and record any observations on the data sheet.

2 Explosion. This must be done in the hood, with the window down as far as possible for safety.
   (a) Ignite the partially filled bottle of acetylene (Number five) as in the flammability experiment.
   (b) Observe and record both the nature of the flame and the comparative violence of the reaction. Acetylene is explosive with air over a wide concentration range.

3. Reaction with Potassium Permanganate; the Baeyer Test.
   (a) Prepare a diluted $KMnO_4$ solution by adding 5 n»L of distilled water to 5 drops of a 0.10M $KMnO_4$ solution.
   (b) Using a fresh bottle of acetylene gas, remove the glass square, add the potassium permanganate solution, and immediately replace the glass cover.

(c) Shake this mixture for one minute, and observe any changes.

(d) Record observations on the data sheet.

4. Reaction with [Cu (NH$_3$)$_2$]

(a) Add 5 mL of ammoniacal cuprous ion solution to a fresh bottle of acetylene. Reclose the bottle and shake well.

(b) Allow to stand for several minutes. A black precipitate of Cu$_2$C$_2$ (cuprous acetylide) should form.

(c) Filter this precipitate through a glass funnel fitted with moistened filter paper. The liquid may be discarded in the hood sink.

(d) Using a microspatula, take a small sample of this solid and place it on a preheated hot plate which will be set up in a separate hood.

(e) Note and record any observations.

CAUTION! METAL ACETYLIDES ARE EXPLOSIVE.

(f) The bottle, the filter paper, and the spatula used to handle the cuprous acetylide must be treated appropriately to destroy any remaining solid. Place the filter paper in a labeled beaker of 6M HNO$_3$. Rinse the spatula and the gas-collecting bottle with several portions of 6M HNO$_3$.

5 Reaction with [Ag (NH$_3$)$_2$]

(a) Follow the same directions used in Part 4 in the preparation of cuprous acetylide.

(b) Record observations.

EXPERIMENT 11: Report and Worksheet

ALKYNES: PREPARATION and PROPERTIES OF ACETYLENE

Student Name: _____   Day: _____

Student Number: _____   Date: _____

DATA

REACTIONS	OBSERVATIONS
1. Flammability	
2. Explosion	
3. Baeyer Test	
4. $[Cu(NH_3)_2]^+$	
5. $[Ag(NH_3)_2]^+$	

QUESTIONS

1. Based upon its reaction with water, what is another acceptable name for calcium carbide?

2. In the reaction between CaC_2 and H_2O, label the conjugate acid-base pairs. Which is the stronger acid? Which is the stronger base? Why?

3. Both the flammability reaction and the explosion reaction involve the combination of acetylene with oxygen. Write the correct equation for each.

    (a) Which of these represents INCOMPLETE COMBUSTION? Upon what evidence do you make this choice?

    (b) Which represents COMPLETE COMBUSTION? Why?

4. The reaction of acetylene with dilute permanganate may be used as a test for unsaturation. Write a balanced equation for the reaction of ONE MOLE of this reagent with acetylene. Write a balanced equation for the reaction of TWO MOLES of this reagent with acetylene.

5. Cuprous acetylide and silver acetylide are very explosive solids. Write the balanced equation for the preparation of each. The (explosiveness of each precipitate was shown by its action on the hotplate. What is the equation for the explosion (reaction with oxygen) on the cuprous acetylide? of the silver acetylide?

6. How is silver acetylide destroyed by the action of HNO_3?

NUCLEOPHILIC SUBSTITUTION SN1 and SN2 REACTIONS

One of the most common types of organic reactions is NUCLEOPHILIC SUBSTITUTION. In general, a stronger base (or nucleophile) replaces a weaker base within the organic compound. This reaction can follow one of two distinct mechanisms, depending on the nature of reactants and the reaction conditions.

The two necessary requirements for nucleophilic substitution are (1)a nucleophile to attack the organic molecule and (2) a weak base (or Leaving Group) within the organic molecule. Halides (R-X) and sulfates (R_2SO_4)are usually considered good leaving groups because they are weak bases.

SN1 Substitution Nucleophilic Unimolecular

Nucleophilic substitution may occur by a mechanism that follows first-order kinetics, with the rate of reaction depending only on [RX] but NOT on the particular nucleophile used. The characteristics of this mechanism are summarized below. The SLOW STEP is the formation of a CARBOCATION, thus the reaction rates follow the same pattern as carbocation stability.
In addition, any factor that favors ionization also favors this method of reaction.

```
(1)Rate = k[RX]
(2)RX reactivity is:  3° > 2° > 1°
(3)Rearrangements occur
(4)Favored by POLAR solvent
(5)Favored by WEAK nucleophile
(6)Racemization.
General mechanism:    R-X ---(slow)---> R+ + X-
                      R+ + Nu -(fast)----> R-Nu
```

In the laboratory, conditions and reagents may be chosen which favor the SN1 mechanism. In this experiment, alcoholic silver nitrate will be used to react with various alkyi halides. This solution is composed of the fairly polar alcohol solvent and the very weak nucleophile, the nitrate ion. Thus, SN1 reaction is favored.

$$AgNO_3 \text{ (alc)} + R\text{-}X \longrightarrow AgX\downarrow + R\text{-}NO_3$$

SN2 Substituion Nucleophilic Bimolecular

This method of nucleophilic substitution involves direct attack by a nucleophiie at the back-side of the carbon atom holding the leaving group. Since this is a one-step reaction, the rate follows second-order kinetics depending on both the [RX] and the [Nucleophile]. Because of crowding during the reaction, steric hindrance is a major consideration in this case.

```
(1) Rate = k[RX][Nucleophile]
(2) RX reactivity: CH₃X > 1° > 2° > 3°
(3) No rearrangements occur
(4) Favored by NONPOLAR solvent
(5) Favored by STRONG, CONCENTRATED NUCLEOPHILE
(6) Complete INVERSION of configuration
```

General Mechanism: Nu: + R-X --[Nu···R···X]--> Nu-R + X:

In the laboratory, conditions and reagents may be chosen which favor the SN2 reaction. Sodium iodide dissolved in acetone creates an appropriate reagent favoring SN2 reaction. The
I- is a very strong nucleophile. The actone solvent is not very polar. Reaction is noted by the appearance of NaX precipitate. (Note, NaCl and NaBr are less soluble in acetone than NaI, the reagent.)

NaI(acetone) + R-X ---> NaX↓ + R-I

Nucleophilic substitutions may occur by pure SN1, pure SN2, or a combination of both mechanisms. The actual reaction simply follows the lowest energy pathway. If two pathways are approximately similar in energy requirements, then both are followed.

This experiment will consist of several test-tube reactions in order to approximate relative rates of reaction. This will be estimated by the order in which precipitate forms. Among the alkyl halides to be tested are:

(1) l-chlorobutane
(2) l-bromobutane
(3) 2-chlorobutane
(4) 2-chloro-2-methylpropane

(5) l-chloro-2- methylpropane
(6) bromobenzene
(7) benzyl bromide

Alcoholic silver nitrate (SN1) and sodium iodide in acetone (SN2) will be used with these alkyl halides to identify the effect of branching, steric hindrance, and bond strength on SN1 and SN2 reactions.

In addition, one experiment will be performed to determine the effect of increasing solvent polarity on an SN1 reaction.

PROCEDURE

PART A: Reaction with AgNO₃ in ethanol.

1) Number seven clean, dry test tubes and place in a test-tube rack.

2) Place ten drops of each alkyl halide in the test-tube bearing the correct number.

3) Quickly add ≈ a one mL of silver nitrate in alcohol to each

4) On the data sheet, list the order (one through seven) in which the tubes reacted as indicated by the appearance of a precipitate. Wash the tubes and place in the oven to dry.

PART B: Reaction with NaI in acetone.

1)Obtain seven clean, dry tubes and number accordingly.

2) Add 10 drops of each alkyl halide to the appropriately numbered tube.

3) Quickly add ≈ one mL of sodium iodide in acetone to each tube.

4) On the data sheet, list the order in which each tube reacted. Wash the tubes and place in the oven to dry.

PART C; Reaction with $AgNO_3$, in ethanol vs. an Ethanol/water mixture.

Place two clean dry test tubes in the rack. Add 10 drops of 2-chlorobutane to each tube. Add one mL of 1% ethanolic silver nitrate to tube 1 and add one mL of 1% silver nitrate in 50%ethanol/50% water solvent to the other. Note which tube reacts first and record on the data sheet.

EXPLAIN these observations.

EXPERIMENT 12: Report and Worksheet

NUCLOEPHILIC SUBSTITUTION IN ALKYL HALIDES

Student Name: _____   Day: _____

Student Number: _____   Date: _____

DATA

COMPOUND	NaI(acetone)	AgNO$_3$(Ethanol)
1-chlorobutane		
1-bromobutane		
2-chlorobutane		
t-butyl chloride		
1-chloro-2-butene		
isobutyl chloride		
1-chloro-2-methylpropene		

SN1 Solvent Effects:

2-chlorobutane + (a) 1 % ethanolic silver nitrate _____

    + (b) 1 % AgNO$_3$ (50EtOH/50Water) _____

QUESTIONS

1. What is the general equation for the reaction of R-X with NaI in acetone? Is the rxn SN1 or SN2 ? WHY ?

2. What is the general equation for the reaction of R-X with $AgNO_3$ in alcohol? Is the rxn SN1 or SN2 ? WHY ?

3. What is the OBSERVED change in the rate of reaction with NaI in acetone caused by each of the following? (Cite experimental evidence)

    (A) Nature of halogen (Cl, Br)

    (B) Extent of branching of RX

(C) Steric Hindrance

EXPLAIN these observations.

4. What is the OBSERVED change in the rate of reaction with $AgNO_3$ in alcohol caused by each of the following? (Cite experimental evidence.)

(A) Nature of halogen (Cl, Br)

(B) Extent of branching of RX

(C) Steric hindrance

PREPARATION OF 1-BROMOBUTANE

Alkyl halides may be prepared by direct halogenation, by the addition of hydrogen halides or halogens to unsaturated hydrocarbons, and by nucleophilic substitution reactions. In this experiment, nucleophilic substitution will be used in order to prepare 1-Bromobutane from the readily available 1-Butanol.

Alcohols serve as precursors in many nucleophilic substitution reactions. Actual substitution may proceed by either the SN1 or SN2 mechanism and elimination (El or E2) is always a likely side reaction.

$$R-OH + Base = R-Base + OH^-$$

Because the hydroxide ion is a relatively strong base, substitution occurs best when a strong nucleophile is used. Halide ions, including Br-, are weaker bases than the hydroxide ion. Therefore, in order to obtain sufficient reaction, it is necessary to protonate the alcohol, thus creating a better leaving group, H_2O.

$$R-OH + H^+ = R-OH_{2+}$$
$$R-OH_{2+} + Br^- = R-Br + H_2O$$

Protonation of the alcohol occurs rapidly. It is the substitution of Br- for H_2O which is the rate determining step. If the alkyl (R) group is capable of forming a stable carbocation, substitution occurs by the SN1 mechanism.

$$R-OH_{2+} = R^+ + H_2O$$

The intermediate carbocation may rearrange, eliminate H+ to form an alkene, or react with the Br- to form the substitution product.

In the case of primary alcohols, carbocation formation is quite difficult, and the SN2 reaction predominates.

$$R-OH_{2+} + Br^- = R-Br + H_2O$$

This reaction proceeds with complete inversion about the carbon holding the -OH group. Because there are no carbocation intermediates, no rearrangements are observed in the reaction between primary alcohols and halide ions.

This reaction may be carried out by treating the primary alcohol directly with HBr or a combination of NaBr and H_2SO_4. The latter combination is preferred because of the difficulty in handling HBr. Fairly complete reaction is assured by using an excess of the alcohol and the sulfuric acid. Sulfuric acid is heat stable, allowing the reaction mixture to be refluxed in order to increase the reaction rate. Sulfuric acid is a strong acid, giving sufficient protonated alcohol for the reaction to occur. In addition, unlike other strong acids such as nitric acid, sulfuric acid causes very little charring of organic reactants.

The term "refluxing" indicates the heating of a reaction mixture with a water-cooled condenser attached above the reaction flask. Temperatures can be elevated to increase reaction rate while volatile reactants are prevented from escaping and returned to the reaction flask. Refluxing may also be used to prevent loss of solvent through evaporation as would be the case in the preparation of a Grignard reagent.

1-Bromobutane is prepared by refluxing a mixture of water, 1-butanol, sodium bromide and sulfuric acid. This reflux produces an aqueous layer consisting of $NaHSO_4$ and H_2SO_4, and an organic layer composed of the alkyl halide and unreacted alcohol. A standard distillation separates the more volatile organic components from the water-soluble substances.

This distillate of 1-bromobutane, unreacted 1-butanol and water must be purified. Any water which has distilled over forms a second layer and may be immediately discarded. Unreacted alcohol can be removed by treatment with concentrated sulfuric acid. The alcohol will become protonated and will dissolve in the sulfuric acid layer. The alkyl halide remains unaffected. After removal of any sulfuric acid traces, the organic layer is dried over anhydrous sodium sulfate and decanted to yield essentially pure 1-bromobutane.

This SN2 substitution reaction is a good example of the many techniques involved in organic synthesis.

PROCEDURE

CAUTION! ALL HEATING MUST BE DONE IN THE HOOD! 1-BUTAMOL AND 1-BROMOBUTANE ARE BOTH EXTREMELY FLAMMABLE!

A. Preparation of Crude 1-Bromobutane by Reflux:

1. Into a clean 5-mL long necked flask place IN ORDER the following:
   (a) 2.50 grams of NaBr
   (b) 2.00 grams of 1-butanol
   (c) 1.5mL of deionized water
   (d) ≈ 25 drops of conc. H2SO4

2. Connect a water-jacketed condenser to the flask for reflux using the rubber adapter with the clamping arm. Clamp the flask and condenser securely to a ring stand.

3. Heat gently using a SAND BATH while swirling the reaction flask occasionally to help dissolve the sodium bromide. When most of the sodium bromide has dissolved, reflux should be observed. When the system is refluxing properly, condensed liquid drips back into the reaction flask and a vapor condensation ring is visible in the reflux condenser. 4. Reflux for 30 minutes. Caution must be exercised during this heating process. Too much heat will cause material to escape through the top of the condenser. Best results will be obtained if the vapor ring is maintained about midway up the condenser. As reflux continues, two layers will become evident in the reaction flask.

APPARATUS FOR REFLUXING:

1....WATER JACKETED CONDENSER
2....WATER OUTLET
3....WATER INLET
4....ADAPTER WITH CLAMPING ARM
5....5-mL LONG NECKED FLASK
6....SAND BATH

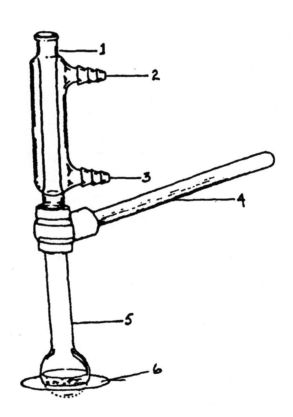

B. Standard distillation of the reflux product:

1. After the refluxing period, discontinue heating and allow the reaction flask to cool until no more condensing liquid s apparent.

2. Rearrange for a distillation using the sideann adapter, thermometer and thermometer adapter. Use a 2-dram vial in an ice bath as the receiver.

3. Distill until the entire upper layer (organic) is collected. The distillate will contain some water, unreacted alcohol, ether, alkene, and the desired 1-bromobutane.

APPARATUS FOR DISTILLATION:

1....THERMOMETER
2....THERMOMETER ADAPTER
3....SIDEARM CONNECTOR
4....WATER OUTLET
5....WATER INLET
6....CONDENSER
7....5-mL LONG NECKED FLASK
8....SAND BATH
9....COLLECTING VIAL
10...30-mL BEAKER WITH ICE

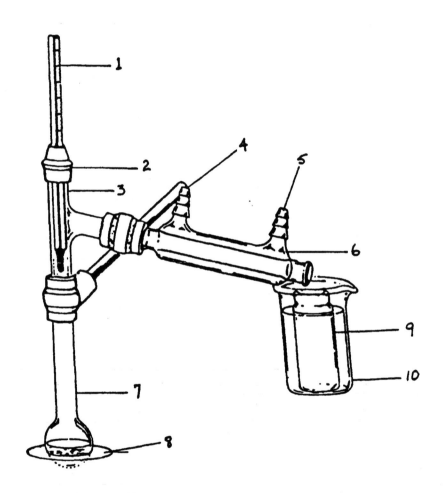

C. Purification of the Crude Distillate.

1. Pour the entire distillate into a clean, dry reaction tube. Rinse the vial out with ½ to 1-mL of deionized water and pour this into the flask as well. Two layers should be observed. Allow the layers to separate and then, using a plastic pipette, transfer the organic layer (usually on the bottom) to another clean, dry reaction tube.

2. Add approximately 1-mL (25 drops) of concentrated sulfuric acid to this layer. Use care since sulfuric acid is very corrosive. Stir this mixture with a glass stirring rod for one minute.

3. Allow several minutes for settling. The acid layer is much more dense than the organic layer and usually acquires a yellow-red color by reaction with any unreacted alcohol. Transfer the upper organic layer into another clean, dry reaction tube using a plastic pipette. If this layer contains small amounts of yellow solution, there is no need for any special procedures. These represent traces of the acid layer which will be removed in further steps. Pour the remaining acid layer into a large beaker filled with water before discarding down the sink.

4. Add ≈ 1-mL of 10% aqueous NaOH solution. This will neutralize any remaining acid, forming water-soluble ionic salts. Stir with a glass stirring rod then allow the layers to separate. Again transfer the organic layer (probably the upper layer this time) to a clean, dry reaction tube using a plastic pipette.

5. Add anhydrous Na_2SO_4 to the tube with the organic layer until this solid no longer clumps. Stopper and shake. Set aside for approximately 20 minutes to allow the sodium sulfate to react with any traces of water remaining in the organic layer.

D. Collection and Analysis of the Product:

1. Pour the dried 1-bromobutane through a hirsch funnel fitted with a frit into a tared 1-dram vial.

2. Record the weight of the product on your data sheet.

3. Measure and record the refractive index of the 1-bromobutane.

4. Turn in the vial with the product to the instructor.

EXPERIMENT 13: Report and Worksheet

EXPERIMENTS PREPARATION OF 1-BROMOBUTANE

Student Name: _____   Day: _____

Student Number: _____   Date: _____

DATA

BALANCED EQUATION FOR OVERALL REACTION

_____

Mass of NaBr used .... _____ mg _____ moles

Mass of 1-BuOH used .... _____ mg _____ moles

Mass of 1-Bu-Br recovered .... _____ mg

THEORETICAL YIELD 1-BU-Br .... _____ mg
(show calculations)

PERCENT YIELD ._____

REFERENCE R.I._____

OBSERVED R.I._____

QUESTIONS

1. What is the MECHANISM for this conversion of 1-BuOH to 1-BuBr?

2. What are the probable BY-PRODUCTS in this reaction ?

3. Explain the purpose of each of the following substances in the purification of the crude product mixture. Use equations as needed.

(A) Cone. H_2SO_4

(B) 10 % NaOH

(C) Anhydrous Na_2SO_4

4. What are the CHARACTERISTICS of the SN_2 reaction ?

THEORY INFRARED SPECTROSCOPY

Infrared spectroscopy is one of the many tools used by organic chemists to identify specific compounds. Like other forms of spectroscopy, it measures absorbance (or resonance) with radiation of specific frequency. Infrared spectroscopy is nondestructive and uses a very small amount of sample.

All electromagnetic radiation travels at the speed of light. It is comprised of various types of radiation, differing from each other in wavelength. Each different wavelength represents a different frequency and a different energy. These relationships are expressed by the equations below.

frequency = speed of light/wavelength   nu = c/lambda

▲energy = Planck's constant x frequency   ▲E = h x nu

Infrared spectroscopy is concerned with electromagnetic radiation of longer wavelength (and lower energy) than visible radiation. This is sometimes called "heat" radiation. The typical range of wavelengths measured is from 2.5 to 15 microns. (1 micron = 10^{-4} cm) This scale may also be expressed in frequency units called wave numbers (units cm^{-1}), from 4000 cm^{-1} to 650 cm^{-1}.

When a molecule absorbs radiation, it gains energy. How much energy the molecule gains depends on the frequency of the absorbed radiation. What changes occur within the molecule depend on how much energy is absorbed. Visible radiation causes electrons to go to higher energy levels. Infrared radiation causes changes in vibration such as stretching and bending but does not break bonds or cause permanent molecular change.

Covalent bonds in organic molecules can be considered to act as springs which hold atoms together. Hooke's law states that the stretching vibration of a spring is proportional to the strength of the spring and inversely proportional to the masses connected by the spring. When IR frequency is the same as a natural vibrating frequency of the covalent bond (spring), then that frequency of IR radiation is absorbed and the amplitude of the vibration increases.

Since covalent bond strengths are relatively constant from molecule to molecule, the presence or absence of a particular bond type can be determined by the presence or absence of a particular IR absorption band.

Infrared spectra are generally rather complex. They represent all allowed vibrational modes for a particular molecule. The intensity of an absorbance is not proportional to the number of bonds that give that absorbance. It is, however, related to the change in the dipole moment caused by stretching the bond.

Lower energy peaks (less than 1250 cm^{-1}) are often caused by a combination of vibrations rather than a single type of bond or functional group. However, each different organic molecule produces a different spectrum. Thus, although complex, an IR spectrum is very useful in the identification of organic compounds. Charts that correlate the absorbance regions with bond types are used routinely by beginning organic students, chemical professionals, and researchers.

An infrared spectrophotometer consists of several parts. A light source is needed to provide the appropriate frequencies. This nay be a tungsten filament or a laser. If the light source is a tungsten filament, it is accompanied by a wavelength selector such as a diffraction grating or a prism. The sample is scanned at various wavelengths. If the light source is a laser, the sample is scanned instantaneously at all wavelengths and the resulting signals are analyzed by a computer program using Fourier transform equations.

The sample is placed in the path of this radiation using a sample holder. Salt (NaCI) plates work very well for liquids. The salt does not absorb in the infrared region. Solids may be scanned in solution using NaCI plates or fused with KBr to form thin pellets. IR spectra of gases are obtained by using special gas cells and cell-holders.

A detector measures radiation after it has passed through the sample and an electronic signal operates a recording device to produce the spectrum.

Certain rules can be helpful when an IR spectrum is being used to identify an organic compound.

(1) Carefully note what absorbances are present in the higher energy region, (above 1250 cm^{-1})
(2) Place as much importance on absorbances that are NOT present as on those which are.
(3) Include all aborbances for each functional group. IE; for C-O-H, check to 0-H region AND the C-0 region.
This laboratory consists of a written exercise as well as the identification of an unknown compound.

PROCEDURE

1. Obtain an unknown from the instructor. Record the number on your data sheet.

2. Measure and record its physical properties

    (a) Appearance

    (b) Test tube boiling point.

    (c) Refractive index.

3. Run the FTIR spectrum of the sample as demonstrated.

4. Analyze the spectrum.

5. Summarize the physical and spectral information to identify the unknown.

6. Identify at least FOUR ABSORBANCES in the spectrum below. What functional group is present in this compound?

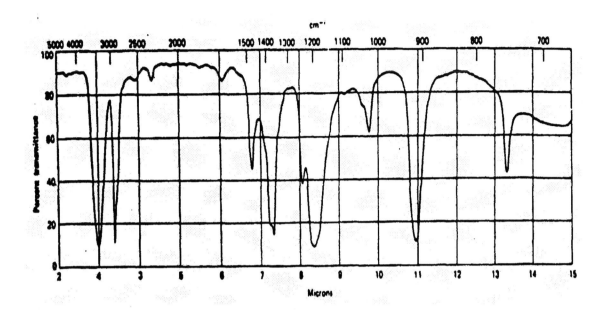

EXPERIMENT 14: Report and Worksheet

INFRARED SPECTROSCOPY

Student Name: _____   Day: _____

Student Number: _____   Date: _____

DATA

UNKNOWN NUMBER : _____

PHYSICAL PROPERTIES:

COLOR _____
BOILING POINT _____
REFRACTIVE INDEX _____

	POSSIBLE CHOICES	BP(ref)	RI(ref)
1			
2			
3			

ANALYSIS OF IR SPECTRUM

ABSORBANCE RANGE	STRUCTURAL INDICATION

IDENTITY OF UNKNOWN: _____

QUESTIONS

1. What exactly does the IR spectrum measure?

2. What THREE rules should be applied to all IR analyses?

3. What are the distinguishing absorbances for the following?

(a) saturated alkanes

(b) alkenes

(c) alkynes

(d) aromatic hydrocarbons

4.(a) How are PRIMARY, SECONDARY, TERTIARY and AROMATIC ALCOHOLS distinguished in the IR spectrum?

(b) how are they similar?

5. A strong absorbance around 1700 cm^{-1} is characteristic of the C=O bond feature. Which FUNCTIONAL GROUPS will give this absorbance?

6. Which bonds show absorbances between 3000 and 4000 cm^{-1} ?

THEORY NMR SPECTROSCOPY

Nuclear Magnetic Resonance (NMR) Spectroscopy is one of the most useful tools of the organic chemist for identification of structure. There are two types of NMR spectra that are used for identification, PMR and CMR. PMR (Proton Magnetic Resonance) specifically measures and helps to classify the various types of hydrogens (protons) present in an organic molecule. CMR (Carbon-13 Magnetic Resonance) measures and helps to classify the various carbons in an organic molecule. Of recent vintage is the use of MRI (Magnetic Resonance Imaging) by health-care professionals specifically for better definition of soft-tissue abnormalities.

PMR

A proton represents a spinning electrical charge similar to that of an electron. Protons have two spin states. In the presence of a magnetic field, a majority of the protons in a sample occupy the lower energy spin state which is aligned with the applied magnetic field. If the sample is kept in a magnetic field and scanned with the right amount of energy, the proton will absorb this energy (resonate) and go into the higher energy spin state. This higher energy state is aligned against the applied magnetic field. This energy difference is quite small, in the radiowave frequency range.

As the strength of the applied magnetic field is increased, the difference in energy between the two spin states also increases. Thus, the energy required to "flip" a proton increases as the magnetic field is increased.

The NMR spectroscope works at a constant field strength. (In reality the radiofrequency is kept constant and the magnetic field strength is varied, but the principle remains the same.) Thus, it would seem that all protons in a molecule should absorb at the same amount of energy and produce one signal. This is NOT the case, however. A proton does not exist in a vacuum. It exists in a magnetic environment which is determined by both the external APPLIED field and the internal INDUCED fields created because of molecular structure.

Internal induced fields may be classified as local diamagnetic effects or anisotropy effects. Diamagnetic shielding occurs when the electrons around the carbon to which the proton is attached "shield" the proton and keep it from feeling the full effect of the applied magnetic field. The carbon's electrons are caused to circulate, creating a small induced field which opposes the applied field. Nearby electronegative elements shift electron density away from the carbon and thus "deshield" any protons attached to that carbon.

Anisotropy effects are NONUNIFORM induced magnetic fields that are created by the circulation of π electrons. These fields also oppose the \pplied field and create vastly different magnetic environments for protons J.n different portions of the nonuniform field.

In summary, if a molecule is placed in a uniform magnetic field, H / each magnetically different proton requires the same TOTAL amount of energy to "flip". However, because of local diamagnetic shielding and anisotropy effects, each group of magnetically different protons will require a different H . The total energy difference, *E, between State 1 and State 2 will be the sum of H and H,^, the applied and the induced fields.

$$\Delta E \;=\; H_{app} \;+\; H_{ind}$$

When the induced field is in the SAME DIRECTION as the applied field at the prolongs location, the proton is DESHIELDED and requires lower applied energy to "flip". When the induced field is in the OPPOSITE DIRECTION from the applied field at the location of the proton, the proton is SHIELDED and requires higher applied energy to "flip". (Note: all induced fields oppose the applied magnetic field. However, the location of the proton within the induced field determines shielding or deshielding effects.)

Magnetically equivalent protons are also chemically equivalent. Magnetically nonequivalent protons are also chemically different. Thus, chemically different protons will produce different signals on an NMR spectrum.

The scale used in NMR spectroscopy is developed to be independent of the applied field strength. It is based on ppm (parts per million) shift from a standard signal. The standard chosen is TMS (tetramethylsilane) which has stronger diamagnetic shielding than most organic molecules. The location of this signal is assigned a ZERO delta (6) ppro value. This represents the MAXIMUM applied field. Signals appearing at low S values are shielded anc[require high applied field strength. Signals appearing at high S values are deshielded, requiring low applied field strengths.

Thus, the following information may be obtained from a PMR spectrum:

(1) NUMBER OF SIGNALS = indicates the number of chemically different protons in the molecule.
(2) LOCATION OF SIGNALS - indicates the approximate magnetic (chemical) environment of each group of protons.
(3) INTENSITY OF SIGNALS - indicates the relative proportion of each type of proton.
(4) SIGNAL SPLITTING - indicates the number of adjacent nonequivalent protons.

Signal intensity is a relative measurement. If only one type of proton is present in a molecule, only one signal will be obtained. If two signals are obtained with the relative intensities of 1:2, the actual number of protons in the sample may be 1:2, 2:4, 3:6, and so on.

The splitting of a signal depends upon adjacent protons which are chemically different from the protons which are giving the signal. The, general rule is that a particular signal will appear as (J+1) lines of equal separation where J is the number of adjacent protons.

#Adjacent Hs	Signal Appearance	Intensity
zero	singlet	
1	doublet	1 : 1
2	triplet	1 : 2 : 1
3	quartet	1 : 3 : 3 : 1

After some practice, many PMR spectra can be interpreted to ascertain molecular structure. Correlation charts exist which help identify specific types of chemical environments and the expected δ ranges.

CMR

C-13 Magnetic Resonance is also used extensively in structure elucidation. The C--13 nucleus is similar to the proton nucleus in its interaction with a magnetic field. Although only a 1 % of carbon atoms found in naturally occurring compounds are C-13, this is sufficient for measurement.

In fact, this low natural abundance of the C-13 isotope has several effects in CMR spectral analysis. In general, only adjacent nuclei couple with each other. Usually C-13's are NOT found adjacent to each other in the same molecule (although they are found at each different locations within the molecule in different molecules in the sample). Thus, the spectrum is simplified due to the absence of C-13 coupling. Another CMR spectrum effect is due to the low abundance of C-13 in nature. The CMR signal intensity is NOT proportional to the number of carbons producing the signal.

CMR spectra can be obtained in two .different ways. In the PROTON-DECOUPLED spectrum, all carbon signals appear as singlets. In the PROTON-COUPLED spectrum, the C-13 nucleus is split by attached protons. Generally both spectra are obtained for maximum information. The overall information gained from analyzing a CMR spectrum is useful and informative, relating directly to the carbon skeleton.

(1)NUMBER OF SIGNALS - how many different kinds of carbons are in the molecule.

(2)SPLITTING OF SIGNAL - how many protons are attached to each different kind of carbon.

```
"s" = singlet  (no H's)
"d" = doublet  C-H
"t" = triplet  CH₂
"q" = quartet  CH₃
```

(3)CHEMICAL SHIFT - hybridization of carbon and electronic environment of carbon

Analysis of CMR and PMR spectra is most useful in the structure identification of compounds.

This laboratory consists of a written exercise on analyzing NMR data which will be given to you in the form of a handout.

EXPERIMENT 16

Aromatic compounds undergo numerous electrophilic substitution reactions. Nitration is an excellent example of aromatic electrophilic substitution. It is also a very common tool for introducing a nitrogen atom into an aromatic compound for synthetic purposes. Electrophilic aromatic substitution involves (1) creating an electrophile, (2) attack by the electrophile on the aromatic nucleus, and (3) elimination of H+ to return to an aromatic system.

In the case of nitration, the electrophile which attacks the aromatic nucleus is NO_2^+, the nitronium ion. It is generated by the reaction between concentrated sulfuric and concentrated nitric acids (Eq.1).

$$\textbf{(Eq.1)} \quad 2H_2SO_4 \;+\; HNO_3 \;\dashrightarrow\; H_3O^+ \;+\; NO_2^+ \;+\; 2HSO_4^-$$

This electrophile may also be generated by the autoionization of concentrated nitric acid (Eq.2). A much lower concentration of NO_2^+ is obtained in this case.

$$\textbf{(Eq.2)} \quad 2HNO_3 \;\dashrightarrow\; NO_2^+ \;+\; NO_3^- \;+\; H_2O$$

Which method is used to generate the electrophile depends upon the reactivity of the aromatic substrate toward electrophilic substitution. The reactivity of an aromatic compound
(Ar-G) depends upon the nature of the substituent group, G. Electron-releasing substituents increase reactivity while electron-withdrawing substituents decrease reactivity. The SLOW STEP in electrophilic aromatic substitution is the formation of a resonance stabilized cation. Electron-release makes this cation more stable and easier to form. Electron withdrawal has the opposite effect.

Strong, moderate, and weak activators direct substitution to the ortho and para positions. Deactivators direct substitution to the meta position. Halogens deactivate slightly, but direct substitution to the ortho and para positions. These directing properties of substituent groups are also related to the stability of the cation produced.

The following general list of substituent groups and their effect on both reactivity and orientation of reaction is useful:

ACTIVATORS; o/p DIRECTORS

STRONG   -NH$_2$, -NHR, -NR$_2$, OH-
              (amines and phenols)
MODERATE -NHCOR, -OR, -OCO-R
              (amides, ethers, esters)
WEAK   -R, -Ar
              (alkyl, phenyl)

DEACTIVATORS; m-DIRECTORS

STRONG   -COOH, -CO-OR, -CN,
             (acids, esters, nitriles)
             -CO-H, -CO-R, -NO$_2$
             (aldehydes, ketones, nitro)

WEAK DEACTIVATORS; o/p DIRECTORS
-Br, -Cl, -I
(halides)

111

In this experiment, the compound methyl benzoate (3) is to be nitrated Methyl benzoate is an ester, with attachment to the aromatic ring resulting in STRONG DEACTIVATION.

(3) $C_6H_5-CO-O-CH_3$

Because of this strong deactivation, the reaction requires that the nitronium ion be generated in high concentration. Thus, N0,+ is generated by "the reaction in Eq. 1. Because the substituent group is a strong deactivator, product forms in the META POSITION, as shown by (Eq.3) and (Eg.4).

(Eq.3) $NO_2^+ + C_6H_5-CO-O-CH_3 \longrightarrow [meta-O_2N-C_6H_5-CO-O-CH_3]^+$

(Eq.4)   Product (Eq.3) $\longrightarrow H^+ + meta-O_2N-C_6H_4-CO-O-CH_3$

PROCEDURE

CAUTION: Wear gloves and goggles during all handling of concentrated acids.

1. Cool approximately 15 drops of concentrated sulfuric acid in a reaction tube. Tare the reaction tube + acid + supporting beaker.

2. Add about 0.500 grams of methyl benzoate. Cool this mixture.

3. In a clean dry reaction tube, prepare the nitrating mixture as follows: 10 drops cone sulfuric acid + 10 drops cone. nitric acid; mix well.

4. Using a Pasteur pipette, slowly add the nitrating mixture to the reaction tube which contains the methyl benzoate dissolved in sulfuric acid. During addition, maintain the temperature of the reaction tube below 15 °C. Test by touch. After addition of all the nitrating mixture, let the tube warm to room temperature. (About 10 minutes.)

5. Pour the entire reaction mixture over about 5-10 grams of ice in a small beaker. This is a critical procedure for two reasons:
    (1) concentrated acids are diluted for further work
    (2) crystal formation is encouraged.

6. When crystals have formed and all the ice has melted, suction filter the crystalline product. Wash it well with water.

7. Press dry the crystals using filter paper.

8. Obtain the mass and the melting range of your product. Submit the product to the instructor in a properly labeled vial.

EXPERIMENT 16: Report and Worksheet

NITRATION OF METHYL BENZOATE

Student Name: _____   Day: _____

Student Number: ` _____   Date: _____

DATA

mass of methyl benzoate used _____ grams _____ moles

mass of m-nitromethylbenzoate recovered _____ grains

melting range observed _____ REF. 78°C

THEORETICAL YIELD M-NITROMETHYLBENZOATE _____ grams

(show calculations)

PERCENT YIELD:_____

QUESTIONS

1. Why does methyl benzoate dissolve in concentrated sulfuric acid?

2. What is the EQUATION for the reaction between concentrated nitric and sulfuric acids?

3. What is the DOT STRUCTURE for NO_2^+ ?

4. What is the MECHANISM for the formation of m-nitromethylbenzoate?

5. WHY does reaction occur at the META position only?

6. What is the PURITY of the m-nitromethylbenzoate recovered based on its melting range?

THEORY NYLON BY INTERFACIAL POLYMERIZATION

Macromolecules or polymers are formed from the union of smaller molecules, called monomers. This process is called polymerization. When this process is accompanied by the elimination of small molecules such as water or ammonia, it is called CONDENSATION polymerization. When this process occurs by simple addition of unsaturated or cyclic molecules, it is called ADDITION polymerization.

The specific reaction studied in this experiment is the formation of Nylon 6-10 by the process of CONDENSATION. This form of nylon was one of the first synthetic polymers. It is formed by nucleophilic acyl substitution between an acid chloride R-CO-Cl and an amine R□-NH$_2$. The amine attacks the carbonyl carbon pushing out Cl- to form a protonated amide. After the transfer of H+, the neutral amide, R-CO-NHR□ and HCl are produced. (HCl in a solution of NaOH forms water and NaCl.) The amide linkage is relatively stable. In order to achieve polymerization, this reaction must link both ends of the molecules together. Thus, effective polymerization occurs when the acid chloride and the amine are DIFUNCTIONAL.

The specific compounds required to prepare Nylon 6-10 are sebacoyl chloride and 1,6-diaminohexane. Sebacoyl chloride has the structure indicated below:

$$
\begin{array}{c}
\quad\quad\quad O \quad\quad\quad\quad\quad\quad\quad\quad\quad\quad\quad\quad\quad O \\
\quad\quad\quad \| \quad\quad\quad\quad\quad\quad\quad\quad\quad\quad\quad\quad\quad \| \\
Cl\text{-}C\text{-}HCH\text{-}HCH\text{-}HCH\text{-}HCH\text{-}HCH\text{-}HCH\text{-}HCH\text{-}HCH\text{-}C\text{-}Cl
\end{array}
$$

Notice that there are TEN carbon atoms in the sebacoyl chloride. Each end of this large molecule is capable of undergoing nucleophilic acyl substitution to form the amide linkage.

The 1,6-diaminohexane has the structure shown below. Notice that it contains SIX carbons, hence the name Nylon 6-10.

$$
\begin{array}{c}
H \quad\quad\quad\quad\quad\quad\quad\quad\quad\quad\quad\quad\quad H \\
| \quad\quad\quad\quad\quad\quad\quad\quad\quad\quad\quad\quad\quad | \\
:N\text{-}HCH\text{-}HCH\text{-}HCH\text{-}HCH\text{-}HCH\text{-}HCH\text{-}N: \\
| \quad\quad\quad\quad\quad\quad\quad\quad\quad\quad\quad\quad\quad | \\
H \quad\quad\quad\quad\quad\quad\quad\quad\quad\quad\quad\quad\quad H
\end{array}
$$

The reaction between these two compounds results in the formation of a linear polyamide which can be represented as:

$$
[\text{-NH-}(CH_2)_6\text{-NH-CO-}(CH_2)_8\text{-CO-NH-}(CH_2)_6\text{-NH-CO-}(CH_2)_8\text{-CO-}]
$$

Notice that the repeating unit is shown in bold print.

This reaction is carried out by interfacial polymerization. This involves the careful layering of two immiscible liquids. One liquid, dichlororoethane, serves to dissolve the sebacoyl chloride. Sebacoyl chloride is slightly polar, but incapable of hydrogen-bonding. As such, it will not dissolve in water, but is soluble in the dichloromethane. A solution of these two compounds forms the lower layer of the immiscible liquids.

The other reactant, 1,6-diaminohexane, is dissolved in-aqueous NaOH to form the upper layer. The diamine is soluble in water because it is capable of hydrogen bonding and contains a relatively small number of carbon atoms per amine group. It is also soluble in the dichloromethane because of its polarity and during reaction it migrates toward the sebacoyl chloride solution.

Once the two solutions are carefully layered, reaction occurs at the interface. If the product polymer is drawn out, fresh solution is exposed for further reaction. Thus, a continuous strand of nylon may be obtained.

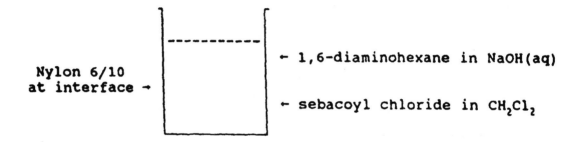

Nylon 6/10 at interface →   ← 1,6-diaminohexane in NaOH(aq)   ← sebacoyl chloride in CH$_2$Cl$_2$

PROCEDURE

Line the inside of a 30mL beaker with a film of stopcock grease. Pour approximately 2mL of Sebacoyl Chloride into this beaker, followed by enough Dichloromethane to bring the total volume up to the 15ml mark.

In a second container, (a small flask or test tube will do) dissolve 10 drops of 1.6-Hexanediamine in 6mL of 0.5M Sodium Hydroxide solution.

Slowly and carefully pour the contents of this second container on top of the Sebacoyl Chloride solution in the first beaker. Two separate layers should be evident with a thin film of Nylon between them. Use the curved end of a spatula to pick up the polymer film at the interface. Continue to curl the resulting string of nylon around the end of the spatula until no more of the polymer will form.

Dip the Nylon into a beaker containing about 15-20mL of 5% Hydrochloric Acid, then wash it thoroughly in water and press it dry as much as is possible.

Determine its weight and approximate yield.

EXPERIMENT 17: Report and Worksheet

NYLON BY INTERFACIAL POLYMERIZATION

Student Name: _____   Day: _____

Student Number: _____   Date: _____

DATA

Appearance of Polymer film:

Characteristics:

QUESTIONS

1. What is the EQUATION for the reaction between sebacoyl chloride and hexane-1, 6-diamine?

2. What TYPE of polymer is NYLON 6.10?

3. The two solvents used in this polymerization are water and dichloromethane.

    (a) What is the solubility of sebecoyl chloride in each?

    (b) What is the solubility of the diamine in each?

4. WHY is NaOH dissolved in the water layer?

5. WHY is the polymer washed in dilute acid?

EXPERIMENT 18

Friedel-Crafts alkyation is one of the most common ways to attach an alkyl group to an aromatic ring. The reaction involves electrophilic aromatic substitution by R+ (a carbocation) on an aromatic compound. The mechanism consists of three steps:

(1) production of a carbocation (several methods may be used)

$$R-Cl + AlCl_3 ----> R+ + AlCl_4- \quad (Lewis\ acid + alkyl\ halide)$$

$$C=C + H^+ ----> +C-CH \quad (Protonation\ of\ alkene)$$

(2) formation of the resonance stabilized cationic intermediate

$$R+ + Ar-H --(SLOW)--> Ar-H + $$
$$|$$
$$R$$

(3) elimination of H+ to form the substituted product

$$Ar-H + -----> Ar-R + H^+$$
$$|$$
$$R$$

Some limitations should be noted with this particular reaction. Since the R-Ar obtained by this reaction is MORE reactive than the original Ar-H, the problem of polysubstitution may occur. Usually, the appropriate balance of reagents can be used to overcome this difficulty. Use of a large excess of Ar-H assures that most reaction will occur with the unsubstituted compound.

Because of the nature of the carbocation as an electrophile, there is NO REACTION with aromatic rings that contain strong deactivating groups. Reaction does occur with aromatic compounds that are at least as reactive as the halobenzenes.

Also, because of the nature of the carbocation, rearrangements may occur. Thus reacting either isopropyl chloride or n-propyl chloride with aluminum chloride and with benzene will produce the same product: isopropylbenzene.

In addition, vinyl halides C=C-X and aryl halides Ar-X cannot be used in place of alkyl halides to create the carbocation necessary for this reaction to take place. The bond between an sp² hybridized carbon and the halogen is much stronger than the bond between an sp³ hybidized carbon (alkyi) and the halogen. Thus, a Lewis acid does not cleave the C-X bond in aryl or vinyl halides.

Finally, even the very reactive aniline cannot react by Friedel-Craft'f alkylation because the Lewis acid which is used as a catalyst reacts with the electron pair on the nitroqen.

```
   H                              H
Ar-N:    + AlCl₃   --------->  Ar-N-AlCl₃
   H                              H
                                  +    -
```

This reaction creates a positive charge on the nitrogen "adjacent to the aromatic nucleus and deactivates the ring toward electrophilic aromatic substitution.

Once the R-Ar has been formed, it can undergo further substitution. The R- group is a mildly activating, ortho-para directing group which exerts its effect by inductance.

In this experiment, benzene will undergo Friedel-Crafts alkylation with 2-chloro-2-methylpropane (t-butyl chloride) using aluminum chloride as the Lewis acid catalyst. The quantities of benzene and t-butyl chloride used favor disubstitution, and the major product expected from this reaction is 1,4-di-t-butylbenzene. Other products such as t-butylbenzene and 1,3-di-t-butylbenzene may also be formed in small quantities.

The 1,4-di-t-butylbenzene is symmetrical in structure and forms a fairly stable crystal lattice. Therefore, as the product is formed it crystallizes readily.

The reaction produces gaseous HCl as a by-product of the substitution. Therefore, special precautions are taken to absorb or neutralize this compound during the reaction process.

```
Benzene..............MW 78.11....density 0.88g/mL
t-butyl chloride.....MW 92.57....density 0.85 g/mL
```

PROCEDURE

1. Using an appropriate plastic syringe, measure 0.80 mL of dry 2-chloro-2-methylpropane into a clean, dry reaction tube. This reagent will be stored in a septum-capped container.

2. Using another syringe, add 0.40 mL of dry benzene to the reaction tube.

Caution: use benzene in hood only.

3. Cover the reaction tube with a septum containing an inverted needle. Fit the open end of the needle with microtubing which is directed to an empty reaction tube loosely stoppered by moist cotton.

4. Cool the reaction tube in ice-water.

5. Open the septum, quickly transfer a small quantity of anhydrous aluminum chloride to the reaction tube and close the septum. The exact amount of aluminum chloride need not be weighed. A small amount equal to the size of a small pea will fit on the top of a microspatula and will be sufficient. This compounds reacts very rapidly with any moisture in the air

Aluminum chloride is very hazardous to handle. Use gloves. Use only in the hood. Avoid inhaling vapors.

6. Mix the contents of the test tube by flicking with the finger. Keep the reaction tube in the ice-water bath. A vigorous reaction should begin within two minutes. The HCl gas produced bubbles through the microtubing into the moist cotton and is absorbed. Near the end of the reaction the product, a white solid, separates.

7. Remove the test tube from the ice-water bath. Allow it to sit at room temperature for five minutes.

8. Open the reaction tube. Add about 1.00-mL ice-water. Mix well. Transfer the contents of the reaction tube to a 10-mL separatory funnel.

9. Extract this mixture with THREE 1.00-mL portions of ether. The ether layer will be the upper layer in each case. Thus, the lower layer must be drained off into a clean beaker while the upper ether layer is placed in a clean dry medium-sized test tube fitted with a stopper. After separation, the lower layer (beaker) is returned to the separatory funnel for the second extraction. In each extraction, the upper ether layer is added to the other ether layers in the test tube.

10. Discard the aqueous layer. Pour the combined ether extracts back into the separatory funnel. Wash with a 2.0-mL portion of saturated NaCl solution (lower layer). This helps remove some of the water mixed in with the ether layer. Separate and discard the aqueous NaCl layer.

11. Pour the ether layer into a clean dry medium test tube. Add anhydrous sodium sulfate. Enough must be added so that it does not clump together. The tube is stoppered to allow the ether solution to "dry". Allow at least fiv minutes for complete drying.

12. Decant the solution into a tared 10-mL beaker. Place in the back of the hood to allow the ether to evaporate.

13. Once the ether has evaporated, weigh the product crystals and record this on the data sheet.

14. Obtain the melting point of the product. Record on the data sheet.

15. Turn in the remainder of your product to the instructor in a properly labeled vial.

EXPERIMENT 18: Report and Worksheet

FRIEDEL-CRAFTS ALKYLATION

Student Name: _____   Day: _____

Student Number: _____   Date: _____

---

t-butyl chloride used..._____ mLs   _____ g   _____ moles

benzene used..._____ mLs   _____ g   _____ moles

Mass of 1,4-di-t-butylbenzene recovered... _____ g

Observed melting range... _____
(ref: 77-79°C)

QUESTIONS

1. What is the equation for the reaction between Aid, and tertbutyl chloride?

2. What is the equation for the preparation of 1,4-di-t- butylbenzene?

3. Which reactant is LIMITING? Explain how you determined this.

4. What is the THEORETICAL YIELD of 1,4-di-t-butylbenzene? (Show calculations).

5. What is the PERCENT YIELD of 1,4-di-t-butylbenzene? (Show calculations).

6. What is the PURITY of this product based on its melting range?

7. What are possible side-products in this reaction?

8. What is the purpose of using a damp cotton trap during the reaction?

9. Why are the combined ether extracts washed with saturated sodium chloride solution?

10. In the IR spectrum of 1,4-di-t-butylbenzene there is a strong absorbance band at 820cm"^{1}. What does this indicate?

THEORY CHARACTERISTICS AND CLASSIFICATIONS OF ALCOHOLS

Alcohols R-O-H are characterized by the presence of the hydroxyl group. Because of intermolecular co-association, alcohols show higher boiling points than aldehydes, ethers, or ketones of similar mass. Among alcohols, boiling points increase with increased surface area. Increased surface area occurs as more carbons are added to the alkyl portion or with decreased branching of the alkyl group. Thus, 1-propanol has a higher boiling point than ethanol (increased C#). 1-propanol also has a higher boiling point than 2-propanol (decreased branching).

The solubility of alcohols in water decreases as the surface area of the alkyl (nonpolar) portion increases. Thus, alcohols become less soluble in water as the number of carbons in the alkyl group increases. When comparing alcohols that contain the same number of carbons, branching of the alkyl group decreases its surface area and thus increases the water solubility of the alcohol. 1-Propanol is slightly soluble in water while 2-propanol is quite soluble.

The limit of water solubility is reached at about 4 or 5 carbons in the alkyl group. However, it is possible to "salt out" or separate a water-soluble alcohol from the water it is mixed with by the addition of certain salts such as K_2CO_3. If an alcohol-water mixture is saturated with such a salt, the anion selectively forms strong ion-dipole bonds to water, leaving the alcohol as a separate layer. Thus, water is separated from the alcohol because the ionic salt bonds more strongly with water than with the alcohol. There are twice as many ion-dipole bonds possible with water than with the alcohol.

Alcohols are relatively acidic organic molecules, being weaker acids than water, yet stronger than acetylene.

Acidity: water > alcohol > acetylene > ammonia > alkanes

Alcohols may be converted to sodium alkoxides by the action of metallic sodium under anhydrous conditions. Primary alcohols react more readily than secondary or tertiary alcohols due to the relative stability of the alkoxide ions in the solvent alcohol.

$$R-O-H \ + \ Na \ ---> \ R-O:^- \ Na^+ \ + \ 1/2 \ H_2$$

Alcohols undergo nucleophilic substitution reactions with ease under acidic conditions. The relative ease of such substitution for primary, secondary, and tertiary alcohols serves as a means of classification. Upon treatment with concentrated HCl, tertiary alcohols are rapidly converted to alkyl chlorides. Secondary alcohols require warming in a boiling water bath for 15 minutes. Primary alcohols do not react at all under these conditions. The alkyl chlorides formed by this reaction are insoluble in the concentrated HCl and form an easily detectable second layer.

$$R-O-H \ + \ HCl \ ----> \ R-Cl \ + \ H-O-H$$

Complications arise from the fact that benzylic and allylic alcohols also react immediately, but yield products that are soluble in the concentrated HC1.

Alcohols are easily oxidized by any of these strong oxidizing agents: dilute $KMnO_4$, $Na_2Cr_2O_7$ in acid, or CrO_3 (chromic anhydride). Oxidation by acidified sodium dichromate is somewhat helpful in the classification of alcohols. Primary and secondary alcohols are oxidized rapidly within several minutes, while tertiary alcohols do not react under these conditions.

Oxidation occurs more easily when the carbon bearing the -OH group is also bonded to at least one atom of hydrogen. The complex mechanism of oxidation involves the transfer of a hydride ion H:- as a critical step. When an appropriate hydrogen atom is absent (as in tertiary alcohols), no oxidation can occur directly. Tertiary alcohols may be oxidized indirectly through the formation of alkenes.

Alcohols which contain the partial structure
$$\begin{array}{c} H \\ | \\ -C-CH_3 \\ | \\ OH \end{array}$$
give positive results in the iodofora reaction. When the alcohol is dissolved in water and KOH, the addition of a solution of I_2 in KI yields a yellow precipitate of iodoform, CHI_3, along with the oxidized portion of the alcohol.

Hypoiodite ion is produced by the reaction between molecular iodine and hydroxide ion:

$$I_2 + 4(OH)- \rightarrow 2(OI)- + 2H_2O$$

The hypoiodite ion in turn oxidizes an alcohol with the proper structure as follows:

$$\begin{array}{c} OH \\ | \\ CH_3-C- \\ | \\ H \end{array} + OI- \longrightarrow CH_3-CO- + I- + H_2O$$

Once this oxidation has occurred, additional hypoiodite ion continues to react with the aldehyde or ketone produced:

$$\begin{array}{c} O \\ \| \\ CH_3-C- \end{array} + 3(OI)- \longrightarrow \begin{array}{c} O \\ \| \\ I_3C-C- \end{array} + 3(OH)-$$

resulting in the final substitution reaction to give iodoform and the anion of a carboxylic acid containing one carbon atom less than the original alcohol:

$$\begin{array}{c} O \\ \| \\ I_3C--C- \end{array} + OH- \longrightarrow \begin{array}{c} O \\ \| \\ -C-O:- \end{array} + CHI_3$$

128

Iodoform precipitates as fine yellow crystals. This precipitate, a result of a specific oxidation followed by a substitution, is an indication of the partial structure of the original alcohol.

Simple alcohols of up to ten carbon atoms may be detected by the ammonium hexanitrocerrata(lV) reagent, $(NH_4[Ce(NO_,)_6]$. The hexanitro-cerrate(IV) ion has a distinctive orange-red color. When an alcohol, ROH is added, one or more OR- groups replace the nitro groups as ligands in the complex ion. The new complex ion formed has a distinctive color. The general equation for this reaction is:

$$[Ce(NO_3)_6]^{-2} \ + \ nROH \ ----> \ [Ce(NO_3)_{6-n}(OR)_n]^{2-} \ + \ nNO_3^-$$

This test is positive for aliphatic alcohols up to approximately ten carbons in length. Phenols or larger alcohols yield insoluble mixtures.

Alcohols react with acids or with acid derivatives to form esters. This characteristic reaction is useful in the formation of specific esters such as ethyl acetate, acetylsalicylic acid (aspirin) and methyl salicylate (oil of wintergreen). In this experiment, methyl salicylate will be prepared by reacting methyl alcohol with salicylic acid in the presence of a trace of sulfuric acid as the catalyst

$$o\text{-}HO\text{-}C_6H_4\overset{\overset{\displaystyle O}{\|}}{\text{--}C}\text{--OH} \ + \ CH_3O\text{-}H \ + \ H+ \ ----> \ o\text{-}HO\text{-}C_6H_4\overset{\overset{\displaystyle O}{\|}}{\text{--}C}\text{--OCH}_3 \ + \ H_2O$$

Lower molecular weight alcohols such as ethanol, methanol, and isopropyi alcohol absorb water on exposure to moist air or are prepared as azeotropic mixtures containing water. The presence of water in alcohols may be detected in several ways. If a small lump of CaC_2 is added to any alcohol that contains a trace of water, a reaction occurs that produces immediate bubbles of acetylene gas:

$$CaC_2 \ + \ H_2O \ ----> \ CaO \ + \ HC\equiv CH\uparrow$$

Thus, evolution of acetylene gas upon the addition of calcium carbide indicates the presence of water in the alcohol. Another way to test for the presence of water in alcohols involves the use of anhydrous cupric sulfate powder ($CuSO_4$) . Anhydrous cupric sulfate is a very pale, almost white powder. In the presence of water, deep blue crystals of cupric sulfate pentahydrate, $CuSO_4 \cdot 5H_2O$, are formed. Thus, anhydrous cupric sulfate indicates the presence of water in an alcohol by a simple color change.

Commercial ethanol is produced as an azeotropic mixture that contains 95% ethanol and 5% water. Absolute alcohol contains no water. Many reagent grade alcohols are composed of a nonpotable mixture of 95% ethanol and 5% isopropyl alcohol. Thus, absolute ethanol and reagent alcohols are both water free and give negative results when tested for the presence of water.

The presence of the -OH functional group and the degree of the alcohol may be determined from Infrared Spectra.

	C-O (stretch)	
	≈ 1050	Primary
O-H (stretch)	≈ 1100	Secondary
3200-3650 H-bonded	≈ 1150	Tertiary
3610 non H-bonded	≈ 1230	Aromatic

In this experiment, some of the characteristic properties and reactions 'of alcohols will be investigated.

PROCEDURE

I. Solubility in water

A. The "Salting-Out" Effect

1. In a clean medium sized test tube, mix 5-mL of ethanol and 5-mL of distilled water. Stopper and shake. Record observations.
2. Add approximately 3 grams of K_2CO_3 to the test tube. Stopper and shake well. If all of the solid dissolves, continue to add potassium carbonate until a slight trace of solid remains after shaking.
3. Observe and record the results.

B. Solubility and Branching

1. Place 2-mL of distilled water into each of three clean reaction tubes.
2. Add 1-butanol to the first test tube in increments of 5 drops. Stopper and shake after each addition. Record the number of drops required to form a second layer or to create a very cloudy suspension. Remember that one milliliter is approximately 25 drops. If more than 50 drops have been added with no separation or cloudiness, classify the alcohol as miscible with water.
3. Repeat Step 2 using the second tube of distilled water and 2-butanol.
4. Repeat Step 2 using the third tube of distilled water and 2-methyl-2-propanol (t-butyl alcohol).

II. Acidity (To Be Demonstrated By The Instructor)

1. Place 3-mL each of 1-butanol, 2-butanol, and 2-methyl-2-propanol into three clean, dry medium test tubes.
2. Add a small piece of metallic sodium (size of a small pea) to each test tube.
3. Note and record the relative rates of reaction.
4. After reaction ceases, add 5-mL distilled water to each test tube. Test each solution with litmus paper. Note and record the results.

III. Reaction with Concentrated HCl

CAUTION! HC1 FUMES ARE HAZARDOUS. ALL WORK MUST BE DONE IN THE HOOD. ANY HC1 CONTAINER MUST BE COVERED.

1. Place 5-mL concentrated HCl into each of three clean dry medium test tubes.
2. Add 2-mL of 1-butanol, 2-butanol. and 2-methyl-2-propanol to each of the three test tubes respectively.
3. Fit each test tube with a cotton plug to absorb the HCl vapors.
4. Allow the tubes to remain at room temperature for ten minutes. Record any changes observed on the data sheet.
5. Place those test tubes in which no reaction was observed in a BOILING water bath on the hot plate for 15 minutes.
6. Note and record any changes after heating.

IV. Oxidation by Acidified $Na_2Cr_2O_7$

1. To 10-mL of a 5% aqueous sodium dichromate solution, add 3-mL concentrated sulfuric acid cautiously with stirring.
2. Pour 3-mL of this solution into each of three clean reaction tubes.
3. Add 10-drops of 1-butanol to one reaction tube. Add 10-drops of 2-butanol to the second reaction tube. To the third reaction tube, add 10-drops of 2-methyl-2-propanol.
4. Shake gently. Note any changes in appearance or temperature. Record on the data sheet.

V. Iodoform Test

1. In a clean medium test tube, place one-mL of ethanol, 5 mL of distilled water, and one mL of 10% KOH.
2. To this solution, add a solution of I_2 in KI, in 10-drop increments. Stopper and shake well between each addition.
3. Continue in this fashion until the solution acquires a tint of the brownish iodine color. Record observations.
   2. Repeat steps 1-3 using first 1-propanol and then 2-butanol in place of the ethanol.

VI. Hexanitrocerrate(IV) Test

1. To 10 drops of ammonium hexanitrocerrate(IV) reagent in a clean reaction tube, add 1.5 mL of distilled water.
2. Add 10 drops of methyl alcohol. Observe and record.
3. Repeat steps 1 and 2 using 10 drops of ethanol in place of the methyl alcohol.
   3. Repeat steps 1 and 2 using 10 drops of 1-propanol.

VII. Methyl salicylate

1. Place 0.10 gram of salicylic acid, 1.0 mL of methyl alcohol and 5 drops of concentrated sulfuric acid in a 5-mL Erlenmeyer flask.
2. Warm the Erlenroeyer flask on a hot sand bath for 2 to 3 minutes with occasional stirring.
3. Pour this solution into a 50-mL beaker containing about 30 mL of water and ice chips.

4. Cautiously smell the solution. Record any observations. Note: any crystals observed upon cooling indicate unreacted salicylic acid since the product is an oil.

VIII. Anhydrous CuSO₄...Test for Water

1. Place 1-mL of reagent alcohol in each of two reaction tubes.
2. Add 5 drops of water to one of the reaction tubes.
3. Add a small quantity of anhydrous CuSO₄ to each tube.
4. Stopper and shake. Wait five minutes.
5. Observe and record changes.

EXPERIMENT 19: Report and Worksheet

CHARACTERISTICS AMD CLASSIFICATION OF ALCOHOLS

Student Name: _____   Day: _____

Student Number: _____   Date: _____

_____

DATA

I. Solubility in Water

A. The "Salting-Out" Effect

Appearance of water/ethanol mixture. . . . ._____

After addition of potassium carbonate..._____

Explanation

B. Effect of Branching
Alcohol   Drops Added

1-butanol   _____

2-butanol   _____

2 -methyl 1-2 –propanol   _____

Explain the observed solubilities in terms of structure.

II. Acidity

Equation for reaction of ROH with Na:

Alcohol	Rxn. Order	Litmus
1-butanol............	_____	_____
2-butanol............	_____	_____
2-methyl-2-propanol...	_____	_____

Explanation:

III. Reaction with Concentrated HCl

Alcohol	Order of Reaction	Conditions/Observations
1-butanol..........	_____	_____
2-butanol..........	_____	_____
2-methyl-2-propanol.	_____	_____

What is the equation for the reaction of each alcohol with HCl ?

(1)

(2)

(3)

IV. Sodium Dichromate Oxidation

Alcohol	Appearance/Temp Change
1-butanol..........	_____
2-butanol..........	_____
2-methyl-2-propanol.	_____

What is the equation for the reaction between each alcohol and the acidified sodium dichromate ?

(1)	
(2)	
(3)	

V. Iodoform Test

Alcohol	Appearance/Observations
ethanol....	_____
1-butanol..	_____
2-butanol..	_____

What is the equation for the reaction between each alcohol and KOI ?

(1)	
(2)	
(3)	

VI. Ceric Nitrate Test [Hexanitrocerrate(IV) Reagent]

Alcohol	Appearance/Observations
methanol.....	_____
ethanol......	_____
1-propanol...	_____

What is the equation for the reaction between each of these alcohols and the eerie nitrate reagent?

(1)	
(2)	
(3)	

VII. Formation of Methyl Salicylate

Appearance/Odor of Product:_____

Equation:

VIII. Reaction with Anhydrous Cupric Sulfate

	Appearance	
	Initial	After Five Minutes
Reagent alcohol..	_____	_____
Reagent ROH+water.	_____	_____

Equation:

QUESTIONS

1. Select a reagent that will distinguish between each pair of compound^ Write equations for any reactions that occur. The reagent should react ONLY with one compound of the pair under reaction conditions.

	Reagent	Equation(s)
(1) 1-propanol 2-propanol	____	_____
(2) 2-butanol 2-roethyl-2-propanol	____	_____
(3) 1-propanol 1-chloropropane	____	_____
(4) 1-propanol propene	____	_____
(5) 2-pentanol 3-pentanol	____	_____

2. Number the alcohols below according to increasing boiling points. Recall that addition of -CH_2- usually increases the boiling point by anout thirty degrees in a homologous series of compounds.

___1-nonanol   ___3-methyl-1-octanol

___2,3-dimethyl-l-hexanol   ___1-heptanol

___1-pentanol   ___2-pentanol

___2-methyl-2-pentanol   ___2-methyl-2-propanol

3. Arrange 1-butanol, 2-butanol, and 2-methyl-2-propanol in order of increasing acidity. What is the conjugate base of each of these alcohols? What reaction occurs when the conjugate base of any alcohol is placed in water?

Order of Acidity: _____

Conjugate Bases: _____

Rxn. w. Water: _____

4. Why do alcohols dissolve in concentrated HCl? Why are alkyl halides insoluble in concentrated HCl ?

EXPERIMENT 20

THEORY ALDEHYDES AND KETONES

Aldehydes and ketones are collectively called carbonyl compounds. They contain the C=0 or carbonyl group. Aldehydes contain the carbonyl group bonded to at least one hydrogen atom as well as an alkyl or aryl group. Ketones contain the carbonyl group bonded to two alkyl groups, an alkyl and an aryl group, or two aryl groups.

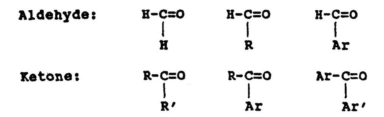

The carbonyl group creates a polar center within the aldehyde or ketone, with the carbon atom being δ+ and the oxygen atom δ-. Thus, the slightly positive carbon atom is acidic and attracts nucleophilic attack. The H- or R- or Ar- bonded to the carbonyl carbon are strong bases and make very poor leaving groups. Thus, the most common reaction of aldehydes and ketones is NUCLEOPHILIC ADDITION. As the nucleophile bonds its electron pair to the carbonyl carbon, a pair of electrons in a π bond shifts to the oxygen atom. Thus, carbonyl compounds are characterized by their ability to undergo nucleophilic addition reactions with relative ease.

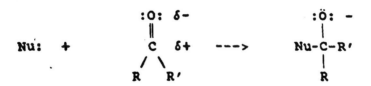

Aldehydes and ketones differ from each other in several ways. Aldehydes are much more easily oxidized than ketones because of the attached hydrogen. Aldehydes are also less hindered at the carbonyl group and are able to react with several bulky nucleophiles.

Aldehydes, RCHO, can be oxidized under mild conditions by:

```
(1) ammoniacal silver nitrate solution (Tollens Reagent)
    Ag+  + RCHO  -(aq. ammonia)-->  Ag↓   + RCOO-
    clear   clear                   silver   clear

(2) dilute KMnO₄ solution
    MnO₄-  +  RCHO  --(dilute aq.)-->  MnO₂↓  +  RCOO-
    purple    clear                    brown ppt.  clear

(3) and other relatively mild oxidizing agents.
```

139

Aldehydes contain a HYDROGEN ATOM directly bonded to the carbonyl carbon. It is this hydrogen that permits oxidation to occur easily. A HYDRIDE ion is transferred to begin the complex process of oxidation. This is NOT possible with ketones. However, it is possible to oxidize the enolic form of a ketone.

Most aldehydes give a positive Schiff's test. Schiff's Reagent is basic, Fuchsin, p-rosaniline hydrochloride, which has been treated with sulfur dioxide to form a colorless solution. When a small quantity of aldehyde is mixed with Schiff's reagent, a rapid color change occurs. The complex formed is deep purple or magenta in color. This test is quite sensitive for aldehydes which are soluble in Schiff's reagent. Insoluble aldehydes give a slow positive test at the interface. Small cyclic ketones give a slight color change.

Most aldehydes and methyl ketones give a bisulfite addition product. A small quantity of the aldehyde or methyl ketone to be tested is added to a saturated solution of sodium bisulfite, $NaHSO_3$. The formation of a white precipitate is a positive test. This particular nucleophile is quite bulky, and therefore cannot react with sterically hindered carbonyls. This reaction can be used to separate sterically hindered carbonyl compounds from those which are not sterically hindered.

$$Na^+ \ HSO_3^- \ + \ \begin{array}{c} H \\ \backslash \\ C=O \\ / \\ R \end{array} \ ----> \ \begin{array}{c} OH \\ | \\ H-C-SO_3^--Na^+ \downarrow \\ | \\ R \end{array}$$

clear   clear   white ppt.

The iodoform test can be used to detect the presence of a partial structure in acetaldehyde and in methyl ketones. The necessary partial structure is:

$$\begin{array}{c} O \\ \| \\ -C-CH_3 \end{array}$$

The remaining bond may be to H, R, or Ar.

When a methyl carbonyl compound is reacted with a solution of I, in KI under alkaline conditions, a sequential reaction occurs producing a straw yellow precipitate of iodoform, $CHI_3 \downarrow$

$$\begin{array}{c} O \\ \| \\ -C-CH_3 \end{array} \ + \ 3I_2 \ + \ 3NaOH \ ---> \ \begin{array}{c} O \\ \| \\ -C-CI_3 \end{array} \ + \ 3NaI \ + \ 3H_2O$$

$$\begin{array}{c} O \\ \| \\ -C-CI_3 \end{array} \ + \ NaOH \ ----> \ CHI_3 \downarrow \ + \ \begin{array}{c} O \\ \| \\ -C-ONa \end{array}$$

The net reaction is:

$$-\overset{\overset{\text{O}}{\|}}{\text{C}}-\text{CH}_3 + 3I_2 + 4NaOH \longrightarrow CHI_3\downarrow + 3NaI + 3H_2O + -\overset{\overset{\text{O}}{\|}}{\text{C}}-ONa$$

This test is also positive for CH_3-CH_2-OH and other alcohols with the partial structure:

$$R-\overset{\overset{\text{H}}{|}}{\underset{\underset{\text{OH}}{|}}{\text{C}}}-CH_3$$

The alcohol is first oxidized to the carbonyl by basic I, in KI, and then follows the same stepwise reaction as the carbonyl compound.

$$R-\overset{\overset{\text{H}}{|}}{\underset{\underset{\text{OH}}{|}}{\text{C}}}-CH_3 + I_2 + 2\ NaOH \longrightarrow R-\overset{\overset{\text{O}}{\|}}{\text{C}}-CH_3 + 2\ NaI + 2H_2O.$$

Thus, the iodoform test is specific for a particular partial structure in aldehydes, ketones, and alcohols.

The structure of an unknown carbonyl compound can be identified by preparing appropriate solid derivatives and by obtaining FTIR, NMR, and UV spectra. Most solid derivatives are prepared by nucleophilic addition of substituted amines followed by elimination of water. The general reaction follows the pattern:

$$G-\overset{\overset{\text{H}}{|}}{\underset{\underset{\text{H}}{|}}{\text{N}}}\text{:} + \overset{\overset{\text{R}}{|}}{\underset{\underset{\text{R}'}{|}}{\text{C}}}=O \longrightarrow G-\overset{\overset{\text{H}}{|}}{\underset{\underset{\text{R}'}{|}}{\text{N}}}-\overset{\overset{\text{R}}{|}}{\text{C}}-OH \longrightarrow G-N=\overset{\overset{\nearrow R}{}}{\underset{\searrow R'}{\text{C}}} + H_2O$$

substituted carbonyl   derivative
amine

When G = -OH, the amine is called hydroxylamine, and the derivative is called an oxime.

When G = -NH-2,4- $(NO_2)_2$-C_6H_3, the amine is called 2,4-dinitrophenyl-hydrazine, and the derivative is a 2,4-dinitrophenylhydrazone. This reagent is generally used to identify the presence of a carbonyl group because it reacts to form orange to red precipitates with most carbonyl compounds.

When G = $-\text{NH}-\overset{\overset{\text{O}}{\|}}{\text{C}}-\text{NH}_2$, the amine is called semicarbazide, and the derivative is called a semicarbazone.

(Note: H_2N-NH_2 is called hydrazine; an N-N- bond is called azo.)

These "derivatives" are generally characterized by good crystal lattice structures and sharp melting points.

This experiment consists of several reactions that differentiate between aldehydes and ketones (oxidations, Schiff's reagent), reactions that identify partial structure (iodoform test, bisulfite rxn), and reactions which are characteristic of carbonyl compounds (derivative formation). Once these reactions are properly carried out and interpreted, it is possible to identify unknown carbonyl compounds.

Spectroscopic information can also be very informative about the structure of a carbonyl compound. The following brief summary may be useful.

IR:	$C=O \approx 1700$ cm^{-1}	$O=C-H \approx 2720$ cm^{-1}
PMR:	$O=C-H$ 9.7 - 10 δ	$H-C-C=O$ 2.1 - 2.9 δ
CMR:	$C=O$ 170 - 210 δ	

PROCEDURE

I Oxidation of Aldehydes

A. With Tollens' Reagent

Place 1-inL of Tollens' Reagent into each of THREE clean dry reaction tubes. To the contents of Tube 1, add 5-10 drops of formaldehyde solution. Add S-10 drops of acetaldehyde solution to Tube 2. Add 5-10 drops of butanone to Tube 3.

Observe the contents after mixing. Then, place in a boiling water bath (on a hot plate) for about five minutes. Record the results on the data sheet. Wash out any silver mirror that may have formed by placing dilute nitric acid in the reaction tube and warming.

Silver nitrate causes stains. Please handle with gloves.

B. With dilute KMnO$_4$

Place 5 drops of 0.3% potassium permanganate (dilute) solution into each of THREE clean reaction tubes. Add two milliliters of distilled water to each tube. Then, add about 10 drops formaldehyde solution to one tube, acetaldehyde solution to the second tube, and butanone to the third tube.

Observe and record the results on the data sheet.

II. Schiff's Reagent

Place about 1-mL of clear Schiff's Reagent into each of THREE clean reaction tubes. Add 2-3 drops of formaldehyde solution to one tube. Note the immediate color change and record on the data sheet. Add 2-3 drops of acetaldehyde solution to the second tube. Note and record results. Add 2-3 drops of butanone to the third tube. Note and record results.

III.   Bisulfite Addition

Place about 2 mLs of saturated sodium bisulfite solution $NaHSO_3$ into a clean dry reaction tube. Add about 10-15 drops of benzaldehyde. Shake well and cool. Observe and record the results on the data sheet.

Repeat the procedure using 10-15 drops of 3-pentanone. Observe and record the results.

IV.   Iodoform Test

`Add 10 drops of butanone and 12 drops of 10% NaOH solution to about one mL of water in a medium test tube. Add the iodine/potassium iodide reagent solution [I_2/KI(aq)] to this test tube in 5-10 drop increments, with moderate shaking after each addition. In a positive test, the brown color of the iodine/potassium iodide reagent disappears and a yellow precipitate of CHI_3 forms. If no precipitate forms, warm the test tube slightly and let stand. If the solution becomes clear add more of the iodine reagent solution and warm again. Note and record the results in the appropriate place on the data-sheet.

Repeat the procedure using 10 drops of benzaldehyde in place of the butanone. Note and record the results.

V. Derivative Formation

A. Oxime

Dissolve 0.50-g of hydroxylaaine hydrochloride (HO-NH_2·HC1) and about 0.80-g of sodiun acetate (CH_3COONa· $3H_2O$) crystals in about two mLs of water in a medium test tube *. Warm the solution and add 20-30 drops of cyclohexanone. Almost colorless crystals of the cyclohexanone oxime should form within a few minutes. Cool the test tube thoroughly in an ice bath.

Collect the crystals using the Hirsch funnel. Wash with a few milliliters of ice-cold water. Press dry.

Determine and record the melting point.

*Hydroxylamine hydrochloride is the salt form of hydroxylamine. A hydrogen ion is attached to the nitrogen atom, giving the cation H3NOH+, with the anion Cl--. This compound cannot act as a nucleophile because the electron-pair on the nitrogen atom is bonded to H+. The acetate ion (from the sodium acetate) reacts with hydroxylaraine hydrochloride to release "free" base as follows:

$$CH_3COO- \quad + \quad H_3N-OH+ \quad ---> \quad CH_3COOH \quad + \quad HO-N \overset{H}{\underset{H}{:}}$$

Once the hydroxylamine has been liberated, it can attack the carbonyl carbon as a nucleophile. Hydroxylamine is usually stored in its more-stable salt form.

B. 2,4-Dinitrophenylhydrazone

Preparation of reagent solution:

143

(1) Weigh about 0.5-gram of 2,4-dinitrophenylhydrazine into a 50-mL Erieimeyer flask.

(2) Add 5-mLs of water and 3-mL of concentrated sulfuric acid, H_2SO_4. (Use caution! Sulfuric acid reacts exothermically with water!)

(3) Swirl to dissolve.

(4) Add about 5-mLs of ethanol. Warm to dissolve.

This is sufficient reagent solution to prepare at least two derivatives.

Place 20-30 drops of cyclohexanone and about one mL ethanol in a small test tube. Add about two mLs of the reagent solution. Shake well and let sit at room temperature. Crystallization of the cyclohexanone 2,4-dinitrophenylhydrazone should begin immediately.

Cool the crystals thoroughly and filter using the Hirsch funnel. Transfer the crude crystals to a 30-mL beaker and recrystallize from hot alcohol.

Cool, suction filter using the Hirsch funnel, press dry and obtain the melting point. Record.

C.   Semicarbazone

Place about 0.50-g of semicarbazone hydrochloride and 0.80-g of sodium acetate in about 3-mLs of water in a small test tube. Warm if needed to dissolve. Add 30-40 drops of acetone. Shake well.

Place the test tube in a boiling water bath for about five minutes.

Remove. Cool thoroughly in an ice bath until crystallization is comolete.

Filter using a Hirsch funnel and some ice-cold water to wash.

Recrystallize from hot alcohol.

Dry and determine the melting point of the acetone semicarbazone.

EXPERIMENT 20: Report and Worksheet

ALDEHYDES AND KETONES

Student Name: _____   Day: _____

Student Number: _____   Date: _____

DATA

1. Oxidation of Aldehyde

Compound Tested	Tollens' Reagent	Dilute Permanganate
formaldehyde		
acetaldehyde		
butanone		

II. Schiff's Reagent

Compound Tested	Results
formaldehyde	
acetaldehyde	
butanone	

III. Bisulfite Addition

Compound Tested	Results
benzaldehyde	
3-pentanone	

IV. Iodoform Test

Compound Tested	Results
butanone	
benzaldehyde	

V. Derivative Formation

Derivative Prepared	Init. Prod.	Recrystallized	MP(obs)	MP(ref)
oxime				91°C
2,4-dinitrophenyl hydrazine				162°C
semicarbazone				190°C

QUESTIONS

1. What TYPE (s) of compound (s) give a POSITIVE Tollens' test ? What is the APPEARANCE of a positive Tollens' test ?

2. What is the EQUATION for the reaction between Tollens' Reagent and formaldehyde ? Acetaldehyde ? Butanone ?

3. What TYPE(S) of compound (s) give a POSITIVE test with dilute $KMnO_4$? What is the APPEARANCE of a positive test ?

4. What is the EQUATION for the reaction of dilute permanganate solution with formaldehyde ? Acetaldehyde ? Butanone ?

5. What TYPE(S) of compound(s) give a POSITIVE reaction with Schiff's Reagent? What is the APPEARANCE of a positive test?

6. What TYPE(S) of compound(s) give a PRECIPITATE with saturated sodium bisulfite solution, $NaHSO_4$? What is the EQUATION for the reaction of benzaldehyde with sodium bisulfite ? Of 3-pentanone with sodium bisulfite?

7. What TYPE(S) of compound(s) give a POSITIVE iodoform test? What is the APPEARANCE of a positive iodoform test ?

8. What is the EQUATION for the reaction of butanone with I_2/KI in alkaline solution? Benzaldehyde?

9. What is the EQUATION for the reaction of hydroxylanine with cyclohexanone? WHY is hydroxylamine hydrochloride reacted with sodium acetate?

10. What is the EQUATION for the reaction of 2,4-dinitrophenylhydrazine with cyclohexanone ?

11. What is the EQUATION for the reaction of semicarbazide with acetone? WHY is semicarbazide hydrochloride reacted with sodium acetate?

12. Which REAGENT (8) may be used to distinguish between each of the following pairs of compounds ? Select a test that gives positive results with one compound of the pair and negative results with the other compound. Explain what will be observed in each case.

(a) 3-pentanone and 2-pentanone

(b) butanal and butanone

(c) 1-butanol and butanal

(d) toluene and acetophenone

EXPERIMENT 21

UNKNOWN CARBONYL IDENTIFICATION

INTRODUCTION/PROCEDURE

The instructor will issue each student a sample of an unknown carbonyl compound. This compound may be solid or liquid, aldehyde or ketone, as listed in the Table of Carbonyl Compounds.

(1) Observe the unknown. Record its appearance as well as the unknown number on the data sheet.

(2) Measure the Physical Characteristics of the unknown.

LIQUID UNKNOWN:

Perform a test-tube boiling point in the HOOD if the unknown is a liquid. Use about one mL of the unknown in a small clean dry test tube. Add a boiling chip. Remember to leave the thermometer suspended ≈ one cm. above the liquid. Record the observed boiling point. Allow at least ± 5*C when selecting possible compounds.

Measure the Refractive Index of the liquid as well.

SOLID UNKNOWN:

Measure and record the melting point. Recrystallize only if advised to do so.

(3) Perform any additional tests which will help to narrow down the possible choices. Follow the procedures outlined in Expt. 20.

   (a) Schiff's test or Tollens test to distinguish aldehydes from ketones.

   (b) Iodoform test for partial structure information.

   (c) Bisulfite addition rxn for information about steric hindrance.

(4) Using the Table of possible Carbonyl Unknowns, narrow down the list of possible choices. List these choices in the appropriate location on the data sheet, along with the melting points each compound's derivatives.

(5) Prepare TWO or THREE derivatives according to the procedures outlined in Expt. 20. Use the unknown carbonyl compound in place of the known. Use about 0.3-0.5 gram of solid in place of 20-30 drops of liquid carbonyl. Purify by recrystallization and obtain the melting point of each derivative. Record in the appropriate place.

(6) IDENTIFY the unknown. List the REASONS for your choice in the space provided.

(7) Attach a small sample of each derivative in the space provided.

EXPERIMENT 21: Report and Worksheet

UNKNOWN CARBONYL IDENTIFICATION

Student Name: _____   Day: _____

Student Number: _____   Date: _____

DATA

UNKNOWN NUMBER: _____

Physical Characteristics

Appearance:	BP(MP):
	RI:

Additional Tests

Name of Test: Results:	Name of Test: Results:

Possible Choices (Based on Physical Properties and Tests)

Name	BP(MP)	RI	REFERENCE MPs OF DERIVATIVES		
			Oxime	2,4-DNP	Semicarbazone

Derivatives Prepared

Name of Derivative	Observed MP

Identity of Unknown

Name:	Structure:

Reason(s) for choice:

Attach a sample of each derivative, properly labeled, in the space below.

(1)_____   (2)_____

CARBONYL UNKNOWNS

BP = boiling point	DNP = 2,4-dinitrophenylhydrazone
RI = refractive index	SCZ = semicarbazone
d. = decomposes	

LIQUID ALDEHYDES

	NAME OF COMPOUND	BP°C	RI	DERIVATIVE MP's, °C OXIME	DNP	SCZ
001	butanal	95	1.3843	-	123	95
002	pentanal	103	1.3947	52	98	-
003	2-butenal	104	1.4362	119	190	199
004	heptanal	155	1.4125	57	108	109
005	furfural	162	1.5261	95	185	202
006	octanal	171	1.4217	60	106	98
007	benzaldehyde	179	1.5446	35	237	222
008	nonanal	185	1.4273	64	100	84
009	phenylacetaldehyde	194	1.5319	97	110	153
010	salicylaldehyde	197	1.574	57	248	231
011	m-tolualdehyde	199	1.5413	60	194	204
012	o-tolualdehyde	200	1.5481	49	193	209
013	p-tolualdehyde	204	1.5454	79	232	215
014	decanal	207	1.4287	69	104	102
015	o-chlorobenzaldehyde	213	1.5641	75	213	146
016	m-anisaldehyde	230	1.5538	39	-	233d.
017	m-bromobenzaldehyde	234	......	72	-	204
018	p-anisaldehyde	248	1.5731	64	253	210
019	cinnamaldehyde	252d	1.6195	64	255	215
020	p-ethoxybenzaldehyde	255	......	118	-	202

SOLID ALDEHYDES

		MP,°	BP,°C	OXIME	DNP	SCZ
021	m-chlorobenzaldehyde	17	213	70	248	228
022	o-ethoxybenzaldehyde	20	247	57	-	219
023	1-naphthaldehyde	34	292	98	-	221
024	phenylacetaldehyde	34	195	99	121	156
025	piperonal	37	263	146	265d.	230
026	o-methoxybenzaldehyde	38	243	92	253	215d.
027	p-chlorobenzaldehyde	48	215	110	254	230
028	p-bromobenzaldehyde	57		157	128	228
029	2-naphthaldehyde	60		156	270	241
030	p-dimethylamino-benzaldehyde	74		185	325	222

154

CARBONYL UNKNOWNS

BP = boiling point	DNP = 2,4-dinitrophenylhydrazone
RI = refractive index	SCZ = semicarbazone
d. = decomposes	

LIQUID KETONES

	NAME OF COMPOUND	BP°C	RI	DERIVATIVE MP's,°C		
				OXIME	DNP	SCZ
001	butanone	80	1.3791	-	116	135
002	2-methyl-3-butanone	94	1.3879	-	120	113
003	3-pentanone	102	1.3922	-	156	138
004	2-pentanone	102	1.3902	-	143	112
005	pinacolone	106	1.3960	75	125	157
006	4-methyl-2-pentanone	116	1.3956	-	95	132
007	3-methyl-2-pentanone	118	1.3990	-	71	94
008	diisopropylketone	124	1.4001	-	88	149
009	3-hexanone	125	1.4007	-	130	113
010	t-butylethylketone	125	1.4052	-	144	-
011	2-hexanone	128	1.4007	49	106	125
012	cyclopentanone	131	1.4366	56	146	210
13	-heptanone	144	1.4069	-	75	132
14	-heptanone	148	1.4092	-	-	101
15	heptanone	151	1.4007	-	89	123
16	cyclohexanone	156	1.4507	91	160	166
017	-octanone	170	......	-	-	96
018	-octanone	173	1.4152	-	58	122
019	acetophenone	202	1.5339	60	238	198
020	propiophenone	218	1.5270	54	190	173
021	isobutyrophenone	222	1.5190	94	163	181
022	3-chloroacetophenone	228	......	88	-	232
023	2-chloroacetophenone	229	1.685	113	-	160
024	n-butyrophenone	230	1.5196	50	190	187

SOLID KETONES		MP,°	BP,°C	OXIME	DNP	SCZ
025	benzylmethylketone	27	216	68	156	199
026	4-methylacetophenone	28	226	87	260	197
027	4-chloropropiophenone	35	-	62	-	177
028	4-methoxyacetophenone	37	258	86	220	197
029	benzalacetone	41	212	115	223	187
030	benzophenone	48	306	142	238	164
031	4-chlorobenzophenone	78	-	105	185	-
032	4-bromobenzophenone	82	-	110	230	350
033	ninhydrin	243	-	201	-	-

(1) SYNTHESIS OF A GRIGNARD REAGENT
(2) CARBONATION OP A GRIGNARD REAGENT

When an alkyl or aryl halide is reacted with Mg in anhydrous ether, a spontaneous .reaction takes place producing a compound classified as a Grignard Reagent.

$$R\text{-}Br + Mg \text{ --(ether)--> } R\text{-}Mg\text{-}Br$$

The Grignard Reagent is a stable form of the very strong base $R{:}^-$, Although the R-Mg bond has a high degree of covalent character, the simplest way to understand its reactivity is to consider the Gricmard Reagent to be composed of :

$$: R{:}^-, \ Mg^{+2}, \ and \ Br^-.$$

The Grignard Reagent is such a strong base that it reacts with very weak acids such as water, ammonia, and alcohols. The relative acid strengths are: $H_2O > RO\underline{H} > HC{\equiv}CH > NH_3 > \underline{R}\text{-}H$. Thus, conjugate base strengths are: $OH^- < RO^- < HC{\equiv}C{:}^- < H_2N{:}^- < R{:}''$. Any mildly acidic component reacts with a Grignard Reagent as follows:

$$R\text{-}Mg\text{-}Br + HB \ \text{--------------> } R\text{-}H + MgBrB$$

Therefore, when a Grignard Reagent is prepared, conditions roust be completely free of any acidic components. In addition, the R-Br itself cannot contain any acidic functional group.

Grignard Reagents also react with compounds that are not considered acidic. Among these are aldehydes, ketones, aci\underline{d} derivatives, epoxides, and carbon dioxide. In each case, the strong base, $R{:}^-$, attacks a partially positive carbon atom creating a C-R bond. The new bond formation is accomodated by the shift of a pair of electrons in a π bond to an atom of oxygen in case of aldehydes, ketones, acid derivatives, and carbon dioxide. In the case of epoxides, the new bond is accomodated by the cleavage of the strained bond to oxygen.

Reaction with C=0 compounds follows the general pattern:

$$\delta{+}\ \overset{\textstyle |}{\underset{\textstyle |}{C}}{=}O\ \delta{-} + RMgBr \text{ ---> } R\text{-}\overset{\textstyle |}{\underset{\textstyle |}{C}}\text{-}OMgBr$$

In the case of aldehydes and ketones, the initial product is the anion (or salt) of an alcohol. Protonation yields the alcohol as a product.

Reaction with carbon dioxide fits this pattern as well:

$$O{=}C{=}O + R\text{-}MgBr \text{ -----> } O{=}\overset{\textstyle R}{\underset{\textstyle |}{C}}$$
$$OMgBr$$

In this case, the product is the anion of a carboxylic acid. Acidification produces the molecular acid, RCOOH.

When a Grignard Reagent reacts with the derivative of a carboxylic acid. R-CO-Z, where Z nay be -OR' (eater), -Cl (acid chloride), or -OCO&-(anhydride), two Boles of the Grignard Reagent are needed. One mol{ substitutes for the leaving group (Z) . The second mole of reagent adds to the C=0. Thus reaction with R-CO-Z follows the pattern:

$$\underset{\underset{R\text{-}C\text{-}Z}{\overset{\parallel}{}}}{\overset{O}{}} + 2R'MgBr \longrightarrow \underset{\underset{R'}{\overset{OMgBr}{R\text{-}C\text{-}R'}}}{} + MgBr2$$

RCOOH and RCO-NH$_2$ react with RMgBr as acids. These compounds DO NOT undergo nucleophilic addition by Grignard Reagents.

Grignard Reagents react with epoxides as follows:

$$R\text{-}MgBr + \underset{O}{\overset{H\quad H}{HC\text{---}CH}} \longrightarrow R\text{-}CH_2\text{-}CH_2\text{-}OMgBr$$

Acidification produces a primary alcohol which is two carbons larger than the original Grignard Reagent.

In general, to prepare a Grignard Reagent, conditions must be acid free. In addition, the alkyl halide used cannot contain any C=0, C≡N, or other multiple bond. Otherwise, once formed, the reagent reacts intramolecularly. Despite all the limitations in preparing a Grignard Reagent, it is still the most convenient way to synthesize certain alcohols and large molecules.

In this experiment, bromobenzene will be reacted with Mg in ether to produce phenylmagnesium bromide. This Grignard Reagent will then be carbonated by reaction with dry ice (solid carbon dioxide) to produce, upon acidification, benzoic acid.

PROCEDURE

NOTE: All equipment must be completely dry for the Grignard reagent to form. All glassware and the Mg should be dried in a 110° C oven about 30 minutes. Plastic and rubber pieces must be washed with acetone and left in a dessicator overnight. Plastic wrapped syringes should be water-free.

I. Preparation of Phenyl Magnesium Bromide

1. Remove two reaction tubes from the oven and cap each with a septum. Do NOT open a tube unless necessary to perform a particular task. When the tubes have cooled to room temperature, add a small piece of Mg ribbon to one of the reaction tubes. The mass of the Mg ribbon should be between 70-100 milligrams. Record the exact mass of the Mg on the data sheet. This is the limiting reagent, and it is present in 2.88-4.11 millimoles.

2. Using a dry syringe, inject 0.50-mL of anhydrous ether into the reaction tube containing the Mg.

3. Tare the second reaction tube, septum, and small container on the electronic balance. Into this reaction tube, inject between 525-700 mg of bromobenzene. (Calculate the amount needed for a 5% excess based upon the quantity of Mg used.) Add about 0.70-mL anhydrous ether to this reaction tube. Swirl the contents to mix. Using the same syringe that was used to add ether, remove all the contents of this tube into the syringe.

4. Inject about 10 drops of the bromobenzene/ether solution from the syringe into .the reaction tube containing the Mg. At this point insert a small needle into the septum to vent the reaction. A vigorous bubbling reaction should start within two to three minutes.

5. If reaction does NOT start:
   (1) add a small crystal of iodine.
   (2) warm the tube very gently on the sand bath.
   (3) mash the Mg with a stirring rod.
   (4) Start over.

6. Once the reaction starts refluxing, slowly add the entire bromo-benzene ether mixture. The complete process should take about five to ten minutes. If the reaction gets too vigorous, cool in an ice-water bath. It will need to be warmed to restart.

7. When the reaction begins to slow down, check carefully to see if any shiny bits of Mg remain unreacted. If so, gently warm on the sand bath for an additional ten minutes. Make sure that ether is NOT lost by overheating. If the volume of the reaction solution decreases markedly, replace by adding about 1-2 mLs of fresh ether. Once the reaction is completed, the Grignard reagent, along with some undesired biphenyl, is ready for the next reaction step. [NOTE: biphenyl, C_6H_5-C_6H_5, and $MgBr_2$ can form when C_6H_5MgBr reacts with unreacted C_6H_5Br.]

II. Carbonation of Phenyl Magnesium Bromide

1. Place a small piece of dry ice (solid CO_2) in a small beaker, wipe the surface free of frost using a dry towel. Do NOT hold the dry ice in a bare hand.

2. Remove the pressure relief needle from the reaction tube containing the Grignard reagent. Use the syringe to remove as much of the solution as possible. Squirt this solution onto the piece of dry ice.

3. Add 1-2 mLs of ether to rinse the reaction tube containing the remainder of the Grignard reagent. Remove this solution with the syringe and squirt it on the dry ice as well.

4. Wait until the remainder of the dry ice has sublimed.

5. Add 2-mLs of 3N HCl. This should protonate the salt of benzoic acid to form molecular benzoic acid. The molecular benzoic acid is soluble in ether while the magnesium salt is soluble in the aqueous layer. Stir well. There should be two layers of approximately the same size. The ether layer (upper) should contain the dissolved benzoic acid. The water layer (lower) should contain the inorganic magnesium salt. If the ether layer is too small, add more ether. If the water layer is too small, add more water.

6. Transfer the mixture to a 10-mL separatory funnel. Remove the lower layer.

159

7. Add 1-mL of water to the remaining ether layer. Shake well. Discard the water layer.

8. Add 2-mLs of 10% NaOH to the ether layer. Mix thoroughly. The benzoic acid reacts with the NaOH to form the salt sodium benzoate. The sodium benzoate is ionic, and thus dissolves in the aqueous layer. Drain the aqueous layer into a small beaker.

9. Add another 1-mL of 10% NaOH to the ether layer. Mix. Add this aqueous layer to the same beaker that contains the first aqueous layer. Discard the ether layer in the organic waste container.

10. Warm the beaker containing the combined NaOH extracts on the sand bath to at least 50'C for several minutes. This serves to drive out any ether mixed in with the aqueous layer.

11. Cool the solution in an ice bath. Carefully add concentrated HCl dropwise until the solution is distinctly acidic. Use pH paper to obtain a pH range between 1 and 3. At this point, white crystals of benzoic acid should be formed.

12. Cool thoroughly. Suction filter using the Hirsch funnel. Wash crystals with about 1-mL of cold water.

13. Press dry. Obtain the mass and melting range of the crystals. Record on the data sheet.

14. Submit the remainder of the benzoic acid in a properly labeled container.

EXPERIMENT 22: Report and Worksheet

PREPARATION/CARBONATION OF GRIGNARD REAGENT

Student Name: _____   Day: _____

Student Number: _____   Date: _____

DATA

I. Preparation of Phenyl Magnesium Bromide.

Mass of Mg ribbon used. .... _____grams _____moles
(1 mole Mg = 24.305 g)

Mass of bromobenzene needed... _____grams
(1 mole = 157.02 g)
     Show calculation of 5% excess based on quantity of Mg used.

II. Carbonation of Phenyl Magnesium Bromide.
Theoretical yield of benzoic acid........ _____g
(1 mole = 122.12 g)
Show calculation.

Mass of benzoic acid recovered............ _____g
Percent yield.... _____
(Show calculation.)

Melting range observed... _____ (MP reference = 122.4°C)

QUESTIONS

1. What is the BALANCED EQUATION for:

     (a) the formation of the Grignard reagent ?

     (b) the reaction of the Grignard reagent with dry ice ?

2. WRITE the BALANCED EQUATION for the reaction of C_6H_5MgBr with:
    (a) water:

    (b) ammonia:

    (c) ethanol:

    (d) acetone:

    (e) benzaldehyde:

    (f) methyl benzoate:

3. EXPLAIN the relative solubility of BENZOIC ACID and SODIUM BENZOATE in

   (a) ether,

   (b) water,

4. What undesired BY-PRODUCTS can be formed when:

   (a) C_6H_5gMgBr reacts with unreacted C_6H_5Br ?

   (b) water condenses on the dry ice during Grignard reagent addition ?

5. What DIFFICULTIES are associated with use of Grignard reagents?

6. What TYPES of compounds react with Grignard reagents?

7. WHY is a Grignard reagent so reactive?

ACETYLSALICYLIC ACID - SYNTHESIS OF ASPIRIN

"Aspirin" has been used as a pain reliever (analgesic), a fever reducer (antipyretic) and an anti-inflammatory agent for many years. Chemically, aspirin is acetylsalicylic acid, an ester. It is conveniently produced by the reaction of salicylic acid with acetic anhydride.

$$o-HO-C_6H_4-COOH \ + \ CH_3-CO-O-OC-CH_3 \ -(H+)-> \ o-CH_3-CO-O-C_6H_4-COOH \ + \ CH_3COOH$$

Salicylic acid   Acetic anhydride   Acetylsalicylic acid

(1 mole = 138.12g)   (1 mole = 180.15g)

This esterification is carried out using phosphoric acid, which is heat stable, as a catalyst.

Because the product "aspirin" still contains a carboxylic acid functional group, it is often combined with a buffering agent. Acetylsalicylic acid is present in many over-the-counter medications.

PROCEDURE

1. Place a reaction tube into a 5-mL Erienmeyer and tare. Add between 0.275-0.300g of salicylic acid. Record on the data sheet.

2. Transfer the reaction tube and 5-mL Erienmeyer to the hood. Add a boiling chip, 2 drops of 85% phosphoric acid, and about 0.70 mL of acetic anhydride to the reaction tube. Mix well.

3. Place a 50-mL beaker containing about 20-mLs of water on a hot plate or in the sand bath. Allow the water to become hot (s90*C). Then, place the reaction tube in the hot water bath for at least five minutes.

4. In 5-drop increments, add about 1-mL of water. This serves to decompose any excess acetic anhydride, producing acetic acid. Since the acetic acid vapors can be quite strong, it is important to do this in the hood. Since this hydrolysis is exothermic, the reaction is over when the reactants begin to cool down.

5. Allow the reactants to cool slowly to room temperature. At this stage, crystals of acetylsalicylic acid should begin to form. If no crystal formation is observed, use the standard techniques start crystallization.

6. Cool thoroughly in an ice bath for at least ten minutes.

7. Suction filter using the Hirsch funnel. Use a very small quantity of ice-water to wash and help transfer the crystals.

8. Press dry. Weigh and obtain the melting point. Record on the data sheet.

9. Obtain the IR of a chloroform solution of the product if time permit?.

<u>EXPERIMENT 23: Report and Worksheet</u>

ACETYLSALICYLIC ACID - SYNTHESIS OF ASPIRIN

Student Name: _____   Day: _____

Student Number: _____   Date: _____

DATA

Mass of salicylic acid used......_____grams _____moles

Theoretical yield of aspirin....._____grains _____moles
(Show calculations.)

Mass of aspirin recovered. ...... ._____grains

Melting range observed.........._____°C (Ref: 128-137°C)
Percent Yield...................._____
(Show calculations.)

QUESTIONS

1. What is the BALANCED EQUATION for the preparation of aspirin ?

2. What TYPE of reaction is this ?

3. Describe the PURITY of your product based on its melting range and its appearance. What is the position of the 0-H stretch in the IR spectrum?

4. WHY is concentrated phosphoric acid added ? Concentrated sulfuric acid may be used in place of the phosphoric acid, but HCl (a volatile substance) and HNO_3 (a strong oxidizer) cannot be used. WHY NOT ?

5. What is the BALANCED EQUATION for the reaction of excess acetic anhydride with water ? What smell is observed ?

THEORY DIBENZALACETONE

Dibenzalacetone is readily prepared by the crossed Aldol condensation between benzaldehyde and acetone under alkaline conditions. This compound, 1,5-diphenyl-l,4-pentadien-3-one, is used in the preparation of sun blocks. Acetone is a carbonyl compound that contains a hydrogens. As such, it can participate in the various condensation reactions that involve removal of an a hydrogen. Benzaldehyde, on the other hand, does NOT contain any a hydrogens. The following sequence of reactions indicates the pathway for the formation of dibenzalacetone.

```
          H O H              H O H
          | || |             | || |
(1)    H-C-C-C-H  +  OH-  →  H-C-C-C:    +   H2O      Abstraction of α-H
          |   |              |   |
          H   H              H   H
```

The carbanion produced by this step reacts with the more active benzaldehyde rather than with a second molecule of acetone. Thus, the next step becomes:

```
        H O H            O          H O H O-
        | || |           ||         | || | |
(2)  H-C-C-C:   +   φ-C-H  →   H-C-C-C-C-φ          Nucleophilic attack
        |   |                      |   | |          at HC=O.
        H   H                      H   H H
```

```
        H O H O-                   H O H OH
        | || | |                   | || | |
(3)  H-C-C-C-C-φ   +  HOH  →   H-C-C-C-C-φ          Protonation of O-
        |   | |                    |   | |
        H   H H                    H   H H
```

```
        H O H OH               H O
        | || | |               | ||
(4)  H-C-C-C-C-φ  →   H-C-C-C=C-φ   +   HOH         Spontaneous loss of
        |   | |               |   | |              water.
        H   H H               H   H H
```

```
        H O                    H O
        | ||                   | ||
(5)  H-C-C-C=C-φ  +  OH-  →  :C-C-C=C-φ  +  H2O     Abstraction of α-H
        |   | |                |   | |
        H   H H                H   H H
```

Because a 2:1 mole ratio of benzaldehyde is used, the reaction continues.

```
       O            H O           :O H O             O
       ||           | ||          | | ||             ||
(6)  φ-C-H  +  :C-C-C=C-φ  →  φ-C-C-C-C=C-φ  →  φ-C=C-C-C=C-φ  +  HOH
                 |   | |          |  |   | |        |  |   | |
                 H   H H          H  H   H H        H  H   H H      (2,3,4)
```

The overall balanced equation is:

(CH₃)₂C=O + 2 φ-CHO --(OH-)---> φ-HC=CH-CO-CH=CH-φ + 2H₂O

169

This reaction is carried out in a mixed solvent system of both water (to dissolve the NaOH) and alcohol (to dissolve the benzaldehyde). Yellow crystals of dibenzalacetone form easily and in good yield.

PROCEDURE

1. Place 5-mLs of 10% NaOH solution into a clean 50-mL Erienmeyer flask. Add 4-mLs of reagent alcohol. This prepares the mixed solvent system.

2. Tare the Erlenmeyer flask and contained solution to zero. Add 0.530 gram of benzaldehyde using a plastic pipette. (1 mole = 106.13g; D = 1.04g/mL) Record the exact quantity added on the data sheet.

3. Then add 0.145 gram of acetone using a plastic pipette. (1 mole = 58.08g; D = 0.790 g/mL). Record the exact quantity used on the data sheet.

4. Stopper and swirl occasionally for about 20 to 30 minutes. The solution should become cloudy, turn yellowish, and eventually produce lemon yellow crystals.

5. Once crystal formation is complete, cool the Erlenmeyer in an ice-water bath.

6. Suction filter using the Hirsch funnel. Wash the crystals on the filter with two 3-mL portions of 3M CH_3COOH. Then wash the crystals with several mLs of cold water.

7. Recrystallize the moist product from hot alcohol.

8. Suction filter and press dry the purified crystals. Obtain the mass and the melting point. Record on the data sheet. Turn in the product appropriately labeled.

EXPERIMENT 24: Report and Worksheet

DIBENZALACETONE

Student Name: _____   Day: _____

Student Number: _____   Date: _____

DATA

benzaldehyde used. ..... ._____g. . ._____moles

acetone used. ...._____g. . ._____moles

Limiting reactant: _____
(Show calculation.)

Theoretical yield of dibenzalacetone. . ._____ grams
(Show calculation.)

dibenzalacetone recovered. .... .____g

melting range of dibenzalacetone..._____°C. (Ref: 112-114°C)

Percent Yield: _____%
(Show calculation.)

QUESTIONS

1. How is the synthesis of dibenzalacetone classified according to reaction type ?

2. Write the balanced equation for the overall preparation of dibenzalacetone.

3. WHY does the acetone carbanion react with benzaldehyde rather than another molecule of acetone ?

4. WHY is this reaction carried out in a solvent mixture that contains both water (in which the 10% NaOH is dissolved) and alcohol ? Why can't either solvent be used alone ?

5. Draw TWO acceptable resonance structures for the carbanion produced when NaOH reacts with acetone.

6. What is the relative purity of the product based upon its melting range? What should be the approximate location of the C=0 in the IR spectrum of pure dibenzalacetone ?

7. What happens if:

   (a) too much acetone is used in this synthesis ?

   (b) the reaction flask is not stoppered and some acetone evaporates?

   (c) product crystals are filtered immediately upon formation?

8. What products are expected to form in each of the following cases?

   (a) acetone + NaOH

   (b) benzaldehyde + NaOH (conc.)

   (c) acetophenone + benzaldehyde + NaOH (2:1 ratio)

AMINES

Organic amines are compounds in which one or more hydrogens of an ammonia molecule, NH,, have been replaced by R- or Ar- groups. Amines may be classified as:

(1) Primary R-NH_2 or $ArNH_2$
(2) Secondary R_2NH or $ArRNH^2$ or Ar^2NH
(3) Tertiary R_3N, ArR_2N, Ar_2RN

Amines are quite basic. Ammonia itself has a Kb value of 1.8 x 10^{-5}. Aliphatic amines have Kb values of $\approx 10^{-4}$, while aromatic amines have Kb values as 10^{-10}. These differences are explained by the relative stability of the cation produced in the reaction: G-NH_2 + H+ $\rightarrow$ G-NH_3+ When G = R, base strength is increased because the R- group is electron-releasing by inductance and therefore stabilizes the cation produced. When G = Ar, the base strength is decreased because the net effect of the aryl group is to withdraw electrons and destabilize the cation formed.

The relative base strength of amines can be tested in several ways. Aqueous solutions of each base can be tested with indicators. Several drops of the amine to be tested can be added to $FeCl_3$ solution. If the amine produces sufficient OH- to exceed the Ksp for $Fe(OH)_3$, a brown gelatinous precipitate forms. Because iron(III) hydroxide has a very small Ksp value, this test is positive for very weak bases. In addition, amines are readily protonated by strong acids such as HCl and H_2SO_4.

The water solubility of amines is similar to that of other organic compounds that contain H-bonding portions. Small aliphatic amines are water soluble. As the carbon number increases, solubility in water decreases. The usual limit occurs at about four or five carbons. Thus, methylamine is soluble in water while aniline is not soluble. Although most amines are NOT water soluble, amine salts, being ionic, are generally water soluble.

Most pure amines are clear or very pale in color. Often, stock samples are found to be of various colors, from dark brown to almost black. Amines are quite easily oxidized to form these highly colored products. However, most amines can be readily purified by distillation or by recrystallization. This oxidizability of amines is shown by simple reaction with bleaching powder.

Whether an amine is primary, secondary, or tertiary can be determined by the Hinsberg test. The amine in question is treated with benzenesulfonyl chloride in KOH and then acidified with HCl. The results are interpreted as follows:

Amine Type	Benzenesulfonyl chloride in KOH	HCl addition
Primary	Reacts, but product dissolves in OH-.	Precipitate forms.
Secondary	Reacts and forms insoluble product.	Precipitate remains.
Tertiary	No reaction. Amine remains as second layer or ppt.	Amine is protonated and dissolves.

Often, this test is particularly difficult to interpret because of impurities present in the amine.

Many amines form solid derivatives with the appropriate reagents. Among the most frequently prepared derivatives are amides and carbanilides. When a primary or secondary amine is reacted with acetic anhydride or acetyl chloride, an acetamide is produced.

$$R-NH_2 + CH_3CO-Cl --(OH-)--\rightarrow R-NH-CO-CH_3 + H_2O + Cl-$$

$$R-NH_2 + CH_3-OC-O-CO-CH_3 -------\rightarrow R-NH-CO-CH_3 + CH_3COOH$$

If benzoyl chloride is used, the resulting product is a benzamide.

$$R-NH_2 + \phi-CO-Cl ---(OH-)---\rightarrow R-NH-CO-\phi + H_2O + Cl-.$$

These reactions are examples of nucleophilic acyl substitution. Many times, reactions with acid chlorides are carried out in a basic solution to avoid the formation of HCl. This is called the Schotten-Baumann technique of amide formation.

Carbanilides and thiocarbanilides are readily formed by the reaction between primary and secondary amines with phenylisocyanate and phenylisothiocyanate respectively. Aniline and substituted anilines react well with either of these reagents.

$$\phi-N=C=O + HNH-\phi ----\rightarrow \phi-NH-CO-NH-\phi$$
phenylisocyanate   aniline   diphenylurea

This reaction works very well. However, because the phenylisocyanate is a lachrymator, this reaction is not performed often. Similar in reactivity but less dangerous to use is phenylisothiocyanate.

$$\phi-N=C=S + HNH-\phi ----\rightarrow \phi-NH-CS-NH-\phi$$
phenylisothiocyanate   aniline   diphenylthiourea

Amide formation and substituted urea formation both require the transfer of a proton after nucleophilic attack has occurred. Thus, tertiary amines are incapable of making derivatives of this kind. Tertiary amines are derivatized by the formation of specific salts.

In summary, amines represent a major functional group among organic compounds. They are characterized by their basicity, their ease of oxidation, and by their ability to form derivatives by nucleophilic acyl substitution (amides) and nucleophilic acyl addition (substituted areas).

PROCEDURE

I. Solubility of Amines

1. Place 3-mLs of distilled water in a reaction tube. Add ethylamine in 5-drop increments until a second layer is observed. Record on the data sheet.

2. Repeat the procedure using aniline. Record the results.

3. Repeat the procedure using solid aniline hydrochloride small pea-sized increments.

II. Basicity of Amines

1. pH paper
   a) Place 3-mLs of distilled water in each of three medium sized test tubes. Number each tube
   1 - 3.
   b) Add 5 drops of concentrated NH_3 to Tube 1, 5 drops of ethylamine to Tube 2, and 5 drops of aniline to Tube 3.
   c) Test each solution with pH paper. Record the results on the data sheet.

2. Ferric Chloride Test
Add about 2-mLs of 5% ferric chloride solution to each of the test tubes from Part 1. Observe and record the results.

3. Reaction with Strong Acids
   a) Place one drop of concentrated sulfuric acid on a clean dry watchglass. Add 1-2 drops of aniline. Note and record the results.
   b) Repeat the procedure using a drop of concentrated HCl. Note and record the results.

III. Ease of Oxidation

Place about 2.5-mLs of water and one drop of aniline in a reaction tube. Add a small amount of bleaching powder [$Ca(OCl)_2$] about the size of a small pea. Stopper and shake well. Observe and record.

IV. Derivative Preparation

A. Acetyl (To be prepared in the HOOD!)

(1) Place about 1-mL of acetic anhydride into a medium sized test tube. Add about 20-25 drops of aniline. Warm gently in the sand bath or in a water bath on the hot plate for three to four minutes. This should complete the reaction.

(2) Add about 0.5 mL of water, continue to heat. This should hydrolyze any remaining acetic anhydride. During this time white crystals of the derivative should appear.

(3) Add another 0.5-mL of water, heat to boiling. If all product crystals do not dissolve, add more water as needed. Once the crystals completely dissolve, remove from the heat. (This is recrystallization.)

(4) Cool thoroughly. Suction filter. Press dry. Obtain and record a melting point for the product.

B. Benzoyl (To be prepared in the HOOD!)

(1) Place about 20 drops of aniline in a medium-size test tube. Add 5-mLs of 10% NaOH. Stopper the tube well.

(2) Add about 5 drops of benzoyl chloride. Stopper and shake gently. Benzoyl chloride is a lachrymator. It should be handled carefully in the hood. It should NEVER be washed down an open sink. Rapid hydrolysis increases eye irritation.

(3) Add more benzoyl chloride in 5-drop increments. After each addition, stopper the tube and gently shake it. CAUTIOUSLY smell the tube after shaking. If no irritating odor is present, add another 5 drops of benzoyl chloride. This technique of addition prevents a large excess of the benzoyl chloride being present.

(4) Once the addition seems complete and product crystals of the benzanilide appear, cool the reaction mixture and suction filter using the Hirsch funnel. Wash the crystals with cold water. (NOTE: if excess benzoyl chloride is present, the filtration process will be accompanied by irritating fumes.)

(5) Recrystallize the crystals from hot alcohol.

(6) Cool, suction filter, press dry, and obtain a melting point.

C. Diphenylthiourea

(1) Place about 20 drops of aniline in a medium test tube. Add aboutt. two mLs of reagent alcohol. |

(2) Add about one-mL of phenylisothiocyanate to the test tube. Stopper and shake.

(3) Crystals of diphenylthiourea should appear within a few minutes. If no crystallization is observed, follow the steps outlined below.
    (a) Cool thoroughly in an ice-water bath.
    (b) Scratch the inside of the test tube with a stirring rod.
    (c) Add a little ice-water.
    (d) Wait.

(4) Once crystals form, cool thoroughly. Suction filter using the Hirsch funnel.

(5) Recrystallize from a little hot alcohol.

EXPERIMENT 25: Report and Worksheet

AMINES

Student Name: _____   Day: _____

Student Number: _____   Date: _____

DATA

I. Solubility of Amines

Compound	# Drops	Compound	≈ Volume
ethylamine		aniline·HCl	
aniline		List the relative solubilities.	

II. Basicity of Amines

Compound	pH Paper	Ferric Chloride
ammonia		
ethylamine		
aniline		

Aniline + conc. Sulfuric Acid [   ]   Aniline + HCl [   ]

III. Ease of Oxidation

Aniline + Bleaching Powder [   ]

IV. Derivative Preparation

A. Acetyl

Product Appearance	
Melting Range	114°C

B. Benzoyl

Product Appearance	
Melting Range	161°C

C. Diphenyl-thiourea

Product Appearance	
Melting Range	154°C

QUESTIONS

1. EXPLAIN the observed solubilities of (a) ethylamine, (b) aniline, and.(c) aniline hydrochloride.

2. COMPARE the relative base strengths of (a) ammonia, (b) ethylamine, and (c) aniline. EXPLAIN in terms of electronic effects.

3. Write a BALANCED EQUATION for the reaction of (a) ammonia, (b) ethylamine, and (c) aniline with ferric chloride.

4. Write a BALANCED EQUATION for the reaction of aniline with H_2SO_4. With HC1.

5. WHY are amines often darkly colored? What can be done to purify them?

6. Explain, using appropriate equations how Primary, Secondary, and Tertiary amines react in the Hinsberg Test.

7. What is the equation for the reaction of aniline with acetic anhydride?

8. What is the equation for the reaction of aniline with benzoyl chloride? Why is the base necessary ?

9. What is the equation for the reaction of aniline with phenyl-isothiocyanate?

10. What characteristic IR absorbances are given by (a) primary amines, and (b) secondary amines ?

UNKNOWN AMINE IDENTIFICATION

INTRODUCTION/PROCEDURE

The instructor will issue each student a sample of an unknown primary or secondary amine. This unknown may be a solid or a liquid, as listed in the Table of Amine Unknowns.

(1) Observe the unknown. Record its appearance as well as the unknown number on the data sheet.

(2) Measure the physical characteristics of the unknown.

LIQUID UNKNOWN

If the liquid unknown is clear or only slightly colored, perform a test-tube boiling point in the HOOD. Use about one mL of the unknown in a small clean dry test tube. Add a boiling chip. Leave the thermometer suspended as one centimeter above the liquid. Record the observed boiling point. Allow at least ± 5°C when selecting possible compounds.
Measure the Refractive Index of the liquid.

If the liquid is highly colored by oxidation impurities, it must be distilled. Prepare the same set-up as for the test-tube boiling point. Obtain the boiling point. Then remove the thermometer. Reboil. When the vapor ring is created, perform a microscale distillation by collecting vapor in a plastic pipet and transferring the condensed vapor to another test tube. Sufficient liquid should be distilled to prepare derivatives and to measure the refractive index.

SOLID UNKNOWN

If the solid is white or lightly colored, perform a melting point. If the solid is highly colored, obtain a rough melting point. Try to recrystallize a very small sample from hot alcohol, if successful, recrystallize a large enough quantity to prepare derivatives and to obtain a better melting point. If any difficulty occurs with recrystallization, use the impure solid to prepare derivatives and recrystallize the derivatives.

(3) Use the Table of possible Amine Unknowns, narrow down the list of possible choices. List these choices in the appropriate location on the data sheet, along with the reference melting points for each compound's derivatives.

(4) Prepare TWO or THREE derivatives according to the procedures outlined in Experiment 25. Use the UNKNOWN AMINE in place of the ANILINE. Use about 0.3-0.5 gram of solid unknown in place of 20-30 drops of liquid unknown. Purify by recrystallization and obtain the melting point of each derivative. Record in the appropriate place.

(5) IDENTIFY the unknown amine. List the REASONS for your choice in the space provided.

(6) Attach a snail sample of each derivative in the space provided.

<u>EXPERIMENT 26: Report and Worksheet</u>

AMINE UNKNOWN

Student Name: _____   Day: _____

Student Number: _____   Date: _____

DATA

UNKNOWN NUMBER_____

Physical Characteristics

Appearance	BP(MP)
	RI

Possible Choices Based on Physical Properties

Name	BP(MP)	RI		REFERENCE MP's of DERIVATIVES ACETYL	BENZOYL	φTHIOUREA

Derivatives Prepared

Name of Derivative	Obs. Melting Range

Identity of Unknown

Name:	Structure:

Reason(s) for Choice:

Attach a sample of each derivative, properly labeled, in the space below.
(1)   (2)

AMINE UNKNOWNS
PRIMARY AND SECONDARY, LIQUIDS

```
ACETAMIDE: AC
BENZAMIDE: BZ
PHENYLTHIOUREA: φTH
```

NO	COMPOUND NAME	B.P. °C	REFRACTIVE INDEX	DERIVATIVE MP,°C		
				AC	BZ	φTH
01	piperidine	106	1.4530	–	48	101
02	cyclohexylamine	134	1.4372	101	149	148
03	aniline	184	1.5863	114	160	54
04	benzylamine	184	1.5401	65	105	156
05	N-methylaniline	196	1.573	102	63	87
06	2-methylaniline	200	1.5688	110	146	136
07	3-methylaniline	203	1.5686	65	125	–
08	N-ethylaniline	205	1.5559	54	60	89
09	2-chloroaniline	207	1.5895	87	99	156
10	2-methoxyaniline	225	------	85	60	136
11	2-ethoxyaniline	229	------	79	104	137
12	3-chloroaniline	230	1.5931	72	119	116
13	phenylhydrazine	243	1.6081	128	168	172
14	3-ethoxyaniline	248	------	97	103	138
15	4-ethoxyaniline	248	------	137	173	136
16	3-bromoaniline	251	1.626	87	120	143
17	3-methoxyaniline	251	------	81	–	–

PRIMARY AND SECONDARY AMINES, SOLIDS

NO	COMPOUND NAME	MP(°C)	BP(°C)	AC	BZ	φTH
01	2-bromoaniline	32	250	99	116	146
02	1,6-diaminohexane	42	204	125	155	–
03	4-methylaniline	45	200	147	158	141
04	2,5-dichloroaniline	50	251	132	120	–
05	1-aminonaphthalene	50	---	159	160	165
06	indole	52	253	157	68	–
07	4-aminobiphenyl	53	302	171	230	–
08	4-methoxyaniline	58	240	127	154	157
09	4-bromoaniline	66	245	168	204	148
10	2-nitroaniline	71	---	92	98	–
11	4-chloroaniline	72	---	172	192	152
12	4-nitroaniline	147	---	215	199	–

LUMINOL - SYNTHESIS OF A CHEMI LUMINESCENT SUBSTANCE

Chemical changes are accompanied by energy changes. In most cases, energy change takes the form of heat transfer, and chemical reactions are classified as exothermic or endothermic. In a few rare instances, the energy transfer occurs by emission of light. This phenomenon is called chemi luminescence. The particular compound to be prepared in this case is called "luminol", 3-aminophthalhydrazide. When a basic solution of this compound is oxidized, a brilliant blue-green light is emitted. Luminol is an excellent example of chemiluminescence.

The synthesis of luminol involves several stages. The starting material, 3-nitrophthalic acid (1) is first reacted with hydrazine to form 3-nitrophthalhydrazide (2). The 3-nitrophthalhydrazide is treated with sodium hydrosulfite ($Na_2S_2O_4$), a mild reducing agent to form 3-amino-phthalhydrazide (3). This compound is luminol.

When luminol is placed in an alkaline solution, two H+'s are removed, forming water and a resonance-stabilized dianion (4). This dianion is oxidized by a combination of hydrogen peroxide and potassium ferricyanide to 3-aminodiphthalate (5) . This oxidation process is accompanied by emission of N_2 and a photon of light.

The light-**producing reaction is best seen in a darkened room.**

PROCEDURE

I. PREPARATION OF SOLID LUMINOL:

Set a small beaker of water to boil on a hotplate while you carry out the rest of the procedure.

To a round-bottomed boiling flask or small Erlenmeyer flask add 400ng of 3-nitrophthalic acid and 0.8mL of 8% aqueous hydrazine solution CAUTION!! Heat this mixture on a sandbath until all of the solid dissolves.

Add 1.2mL of triethylena glycol and a boiling chip. Clamp the flask in place with its base buried deep in the sandbath. Insert and clamp a thermometer in place so that the temperature of the boiling mixture can be constantly monitored.

Boil the solution vigorously. At first, the boiling point will be at about 110°C, then, once all the excess water has been driven off, there will be a sharp increase in the temperature to approximately 215°C. Maintain the temperature between 215 and 220°C for two minutes by heating intermittently. This can be achieved by alternately lifting the flask above the sand and then replacing it.

After this two-minute period, remove the flask from the heat and cool the solution to about 100 °C. At this time, crystals of the product may begin to form. Pour in 6mL of the hot water which you had set to boil at the beginning of the procedure. Cool the flask in cold water and stir. Then collect the light-yellow, granular nitro compound by suction filtration.

Transfer this solid back to the flask in which it was prepared. add 2mL of 10% sodium hydroxide solution and stir. A red-brown solution should form. To this solution, add 1.2g of sodium hydro-sulfite. Wash the solid down the walls of the flask with a little water. Heat to the boiling point, stir, and maintain boiling for about 5 minutes. Then add 0.8mL of glacial acetic acid, cool the flask in a beaker of cold water and stir. Collect the resulting light-yellow precipitate of Luminol by suction filtration.

II. PREPARATION OF STOCK SOLUTIONS:

Dissolve the moist Luminol prepared in the first part of the procedure in a mixture of 4mL of 10% sodium hydroxide solution in 36mL of water. THIS IS STOCK SOLUTION "A".

To prepare STOCK SOLUTION "B" mix 4mL of 3% potassium ferricyanide solution, 4mL of 3% hydrogen peroxide solution and 32mL of water.

III. THE CHEMILUMINESCENT REACTION:

Dilute 5mL of STOCK SOLUTION "A" with 35mL of water. In a dark room, pour this dilute solution and all of SOLUTION "B" simultaneously into a suitable flask. Swirl the flask and gradually add further small quantities of sodium hydroxide and potassium ferricyanide solutions in order to increase the brilliance.

NOTE: BEFORE CLEANUP. PUT ANY EXCESS STOCK SOLUTION "A" IN REAGENT (BOTTLE AT FRONT OF CLASSROOM.

EXPERIMENT 27: Report and Worksheet

LOMINOL - SYNTHESIS OF A CHEMILUMINESCENT SUBSTANCE

Student Name: _____   Day: _____

Student Number: ` _____   Date: _____

DATA

OBSERVATIONS

Step 1: Preparation of 3-nitrophthalhydrazide.

Step 2: Reduction of 3-nitrophthalhydrazide to luminol.

Step 3: Oxidation of luminol.

QUESTIONS

1. What is the EQUATION for the reaction of 3-nitrophthalic acid with hydrazine? What KIND of reaction is this?

2. What is the EQUATION for the reduction of 3-nitrophthalhydrazide to luminol?

3. Draw at least TWO RESONANCE STRUCTURES for the dianion formed when luminol is treated with NaOH.

4. What is the EQUATION for the oxidation of the dianion of luminol ?

DIELS-ALDER REACTION

The Diels-Alder reaction is an example of cycloaddition. The reaction involves a diene and a dienophile. The net result of this reaction is to create a cyclic compound by converting two ' bonds into two σ bonds. This increases the stability of the system. For this reason, the Diels-Alder reaction usually occurs readily. The characteristics of this reaction are:

(1) diene must be s-cis or cyclic
(2) dienophile assumes endo position during reaction
(3) reaction involves (4 + 2) π electrons
(4) cyclization process is concerted
(5) addition between diene and dienophile is SYN
(6) six-membered cyclic alkene is formed.

In this particular case, the diene to be used is cyclopentadiene. This is a cyclic diene which automatically has the required s-cis conformation. Cyclopentadiene, however, quickly dimerizes to form dicyclopentadiene, an example of cycloaddition. Thus, cyclopentadiene cannot be stored in a bottle on the shelf but must be prepared whenever it is needed. The first reaction to be carried out is the microscale cracking of dicyclopentadiene.

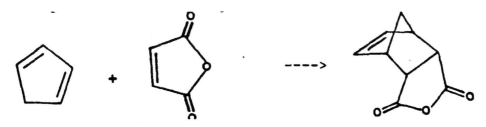

Dicyclopentadiene
(MW = 132.2g)
41'C)

Cyclopentadiene
(MW = 66.Ig; BP =

This thermally induced cracking is actually the reverse of a Diels-Alder reaction. Once the cyclopentadiene has been prepared, it is reacted with maleic anhydride as the dienophile.

cyclopentadiene   maleic anhydride   cis-Norbornene-5,6-endo-
dicarboxylic anhydride
[MW = 164.2g, MP = 165'C]

Thus, cracking of dicyclopentadiene (a reverse Diels-Alder) produces cyclopentadiene which, in turn, reacts with maleic anhydride by the Diels-Alder reaction.

PROCEDURE

I. Cracking of Dicyclopentadiene.

1) Arrange the apparatus in the HOOD as shown below. Place about 2.5 mLs of mineral oil in the 5-mL short-necked round bottom flask. The addition port must be capped with a septum to allow for the injection of the dicyclopentadiene. A thermometer must be properly inserted to measure temperature. The water-jacketed condenser should be used to direct and cool the cyclopentadiene as it is formed. Clamp the entire set-up to a ring stand. Place the sand bath on an iron ring and clamp so that it can be lowered when reaction is complete. Tare the receiver along with a piece of aluminum foil which will be used as a cap. Record this mass on the data sheet. Cool the receiver in an ice-water bath. It is essential that the product be kept cold to prevent evaporation. Have the instructor check your set-up.

1....THERMOMETER
2....THERMOMETER ADAPTER
3....SIDEARM CONNECTOR
4....WATER-JACKETED CONDENSER
5....30mL BEAKER WITH ICE
6....2-dram VIAL
7....SHORT-NECKED FLASK
8....ADAPTER WITH CLAMPING ARM
9....SIDEARM CONNECTOR
10...RUBBER SEPTUM
11...SYRINGE WITH NEEDLE

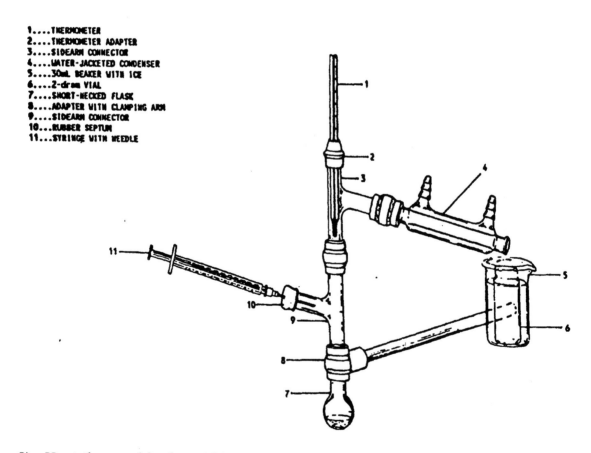

2) Heat the sand bath to 200-250ºC. Check using a thermometer, but DO NOT leave in the sand bath.

3) Using a 2-mL syringe, draw 0.5-mL of dicyclopentadiene from the septum-capped container. To do this properly, first inject about 0.5 mL of air into the reagent container. Be extremely careful about any spillage. This compound has a terrible smell. Stick the syringe needle into a rubber cork stopper until ready for use.

4) When the oil is hot, inject the dicyclopentadiene through the septum on the addition port. Add dropwise so that the thermometer does NOT go above 42°C. The addition process can be completed in about twenty minutes. After all the dicyclopentadiene has been added, lower the sand bath and turn it off. Remove the syringe.

5) Rinse the syringe with a little acetone in the hood.

6) Cap the product cyclopentadiene with the aluminum foil. Weigh and record the value on the data sheet. This may the limiting reagent for the Diels-Alder reaction to follow. Keep tightly capped and cold until ready for the next procedure.

II. Reaction with Maleic Anhydride

1) Dissolve 0.50 g of powdered maleic anhydride in 2.5-mL of ethyl acetate and 2.5-mL of ligroin in a 50-mL Erlenmeyer flask. This mixture of solvents is needed because the maleic anhydride is too soluble in ethyl acetate and not soluble enough in ligroin.

2) Add the cyclopentadiene prepared in Part I to this solution of maleic anhydride. Mix well.

3) The exothermic Diels-Alder reaction should occur. As the reaction mixture begins to cool down, crystals of cis-norbornene-5, 6-endo-dicarboxylic anhydride should separate.

4) If crystals do not form, cool well in an ice-water bath and scratch the interior walls of the Erlenmeyer flask. If crystals form too quickly, they will be very small. In such case, warm to dissolve, and allow to cool more slowly. Large plate-like crystals should form.

5) Use the Hirsh funnel to filter the product crystals. Wash with a small portion of cold ligroin.

6) Spread the product crystals out to air dry on weighing paper.

7) Determine the weight and melting point. Record. Submit the remainder of the crystals, properly labeled.

EXPERIMENT 28: Report and Worksheet

DIELS-ALDER

Student Name: _____   Day: _____

Student Number: _____   Date: _____

_____

DATA

Mass of cyclopentadiene from cracking ..... _____grams _____moles

Mass of naleic anhydride used .... _____grams _____moles

Limiting Reactant: _____

Theoretical yield of adduct: _____

Mass of Diels-Alder product obtained...... _____ grams

Melting range of Diels-Alder product...... _____ °C [Ref = 165°C]

Percentage Yield: _____

_____

QUESTIONS

1. What is the BALANCED EQUATION for the cracking of dicyclopentadiene ?

2. Show how the dimerization of cyclopentadiene is an example of Diels-Alder cycloaddition.

3. Which reagent, cyclopentadiene or maleic anhydride, is limiting? How did you determine this?

4. What is the THEORETICAL YIELD of the cis-norbornene-5,6-endo-dicarboxylic anhydride?

5. Is the product pure? Cite experimental evidence.

6. What are five characteristics of the Diels-Alder reaction?

7. What product is expected if cyclopentadiene is reacted with each of these dienophiles?

1) propenal $(H_2C=CH-HC=O)$

2) 2-butenal $(CH_3-CH=CH-HC=O)$

3) cyclopenten-3-one

4) cyclohexen-3-one

5) cyclohexen-3,6-dione

EXPERIMENT 29

DIAZOTIZATION/DIAZOCOUPLING: PREPARATION OF METHYL ORANGE

Amines have numerous reactions with nitrous acid, HONO. These reactions involve attack by the nitrosonium ion, $:N\equiv O:+$, as an electrophile, at the nitrogen atom's electon pair. They may be summarized as follows:

1° aliphatic	$:N\equiv N:+$ alcohols
1° aromatic	$Ar-N\equiv N:+$
2°	N-nitrosoamines
3° aliphatic	no reaction
3° aromatic	p-nitrosoamines

One of the more important synthetic tools in organic chemistry is the diazonium salt, $ArN\equiv N:+$, which acts as an intermediate in the production of Ar-X, Ar-C=N, and Ar-OH. The diazoniuro salt reacts with various nucleophiles to form the substituted product and N_2 gas. This nucleophilic substitution reaction is thought to occur by a radical mechanism. Some examples of these reactions are shown below.

$Ar-N\equiv N:^+$

(1) KCN, CuCN	---->	$Ar-C\equiv N$ (nitrile)	+	$N\equiv N$
(2) H+, HOH	---->	Ar-OH (phenol)	+	$N\equiv N$
(3) H_3PO_2	---->	Ar-H	+	$N\equiv N$
(4) KI	---->	Ar-I	+	$N\equiv N$
(5) CuBr (CuCl)	---->	Ar-Br (Ar-Cl)	+	$N\equiv N$
(6) HBF_4 , heat	---->	Ar-F	+	$N\equiv N$

A diazonium salt is capable of reacting with highly activated aromatic compounds to form coupling products which have the formula Ar-N=N-Ar-G. These highly conjugated compounds are excellent dyes.

$Ar-N\equiv N:^+$ + $H-Ar'-G$ ----> $Ar-N=N-Ar'-G$ + H^+
coupling product

In this exercise, a diazonium salt will be synthesized and then reacted with N,N-dimethylaniline in a coupling reaction.

The process of diazotization is carried out by reacting a primal aromatic amine with the nitrosonium ion under slightly acidic conditions. In this case

199

the compound to be diazotized is sulfanilic acid, p- ^-O_3S-C_6H_4-NH_3*. This difunctional compound normally exists as a "zwitterion" which is indicated in the latter formula. This process is summarized as follows:

(1) Reaction of sulfanilic acid with sodium carbonate. This creates the free $–NH_2$ group.

$$2 \text{ [p-}^-O_3S\text{-}C_6H_4\text{-}NH_3^{\cdot}] + Na_2CO_3 \text{ --> } 2 \text{ [p-}NaO_3S\text{-}C_6H_4\text{-}NH_2] + H_2CO_3$$
(1 mole = 173.19g)

(2) Reaction with sodium nitrite and HCl. This reaction involves attack of NO+ at the aromatic nitrogen, followed by elimination of water.

$$[\text{p-}NaO_3S\text{-}C_6H_4\text{-}NH_2] + NaONO \text{ --> } [\text{p-}^-O_3S\text{-}C_6H_4\text{-}N\equiv N^{\cdot}] + 2H_2O + 2NaCl$$
diazonium salt

The diazonium salt produced by this process is not purified but is reacted with the coupling reagent. In this case, the diazonium salt is reacted with the highly activated N.N-dimethylaniline (1 mole = 121.18g) to yield methyl orange, an azo dye. This reaction is an example of electrophilic aromatic substitution by the very weak electrophile, the diazonium ion.

$$\text{p-}^-O_3S\text{-}C_6H_4\text{-}N\equiv N^{\cdot} + C_6H_5NH(CH_3)_2^{\cdot} \text{ } Cl^- + 2NaOH \text{ -->}$$

$$\text{p-}NaO_3S\text{-}C_6H_4\text{-}N=N\text{-}C_6H_4N(CH_3)_2\text{-p} + NaCl + 2H_2O$$
"methyl orange"

Thus, amines react with HONO to yield various products. A primary aromatic amine is converted to a diazonium salt which in turn leads to numerous substitution and coupling products. For this reason, diazonium salts are often used in many synthetic processes.

PROCEDURE

I. Diazotization

1. Place 200 mg of sulfanilic acid in a 50-mL Erlenmeyer flask. Add 60 mg of anhydrous Na_2CO_3 and 2-mLs of water. Warm this mixture gently on the sand bath to dissolve the solids. Then, cool the solution to room temperature.

2. Add 85 mg of NaONO (sodium nitrite). Stir to dissolve.

3. Place in an ice-water bath to cool.

4. While this solution is cooling, mix about 2 grams of ice with six drops of concentrated HCl in a reaction tube. Pour this mixture into the Erlenmeyer flask. Stir thoroughly.

5. The diazonium salt should begin to form within 2-5 minutes. It will appear as a white suspended precipitate. Set this suspension aside in the ice-water bath in preparation for the coupling reaction.

II. Oiazocoupling: Preparation of Methyl Orange.

1. Tare a reaction tube in a small beaker. Add 130 mg dimethyl-aniline and 110 mg of glacial acetic acid to this tared reaction tube. Mix well. [Note: dimethylaniline is the limiting reagent.]

2. Pour the dimethylaniline/acetic acid solution into the Erlenmeyer flask containing the suspended diazonium salt. Rinse the reaction tube with a little water to transfer the last traces of the dimethylaniline/acetic acid solution.

3. Stir the contents of the Erienmeyer flask for several minutes. A red, pasty mass of methyl orange should separate.

4. Add 2-mLs of 10% NaOH and mix. Check with Litmus paper to determine if the solution is alkaline. Add more NaOH if needed.

5. Add 1.2 grains of NaCl. The color of the crystals should become yellow as the acid form of methyl orange is converted to its sodium salt in its base form. NaCl is added to decrease the solubility of this sodium salt in water.

6. Warm the solution to nearly boiling in the sand bath. Allow the solution to cool to room temperature and then in an ice-water bath. The dye should separate as orange-colored crystals.

7. Suction filter the crystals. Press dry. Obtain the weight of the crystals and turn in the product in a properly labeled vial.

EXPERIMENT 29: Report and Worksheet

DIAZOTIZATION/ DIAZOCOOPLING: PREPARATION OF METHYL ORANGE

Student Name: ____________________ **Day:** ________

Student Number: ____________________ **Date:** ________

DATA

Mass of sulfanilic acid used. .... ______grams _____moles

Mass of dimethylaniline used. .... ______grams _____moles

Theoretical yield of methyl orange: _______grams
(Show calculation.)

Mass of methyl orange obtained. . . ._________grams
Percent Yield: ________
(Show calculation.)

QUESTIONS

1. Draw TWO RESONANCE STRUCTURES for the nitrosonium ion, NO^+.

2. What is the equation for generating NO+ in a dilute solution of HCl and NaONO?

3. What is the BALANCED EQUATION for the reaction between sulfanilic acid and sodium carbonate ?

4. What is the BALANCED EQUATION for the reaction sodium sulfanilate (product of previous reaction) and NaONO and HCl ?

5. What is the BALANCED EQUATION for the reaction between the diazonium salt; (product of previous reaction) and N,N-dimethylaniline ?

6. Show, by using arrows, the MOVEMENT of ELECTRON PAIRS when the diazonium ion, acting as an electrophile, attacks N,N-dimethylaniline. The product of this attack is a resonance-stabilized aromatic carbocation.

7. What is the purpose of adding NaOH to the red crystals of methyl orange?

8. WHY is NaCl added to the reaction mixture before final crystallization?

9. What is the general reaction that occurs between a diazonium salt and a nucleophile, Nu- ?

10. What product is formed when p-CH_3-C_6H_4-N≡N* is reacted with each of the following compounds?

(1) KI

(2) HBF_4, heat

(3) CuCN, then, H_2 catalyst

(4) phenol

(5) o-methylphenol (o-cresol)

(6) H+, water

ELEMENTAL ANALYSIS BY SODIUM FUSION

Organic compound identification has become very sophisticated with the use of mass spectrography, FTIR, and other instrumental techniques. Since most organic compounds contain CARBON, HYDROGEN, and OXYGEN, the relative percentage of each element can also be determined by the chemical technique of complete combustion of a weighed sample of the compound. This produces the compounds CO_2 and H_2O which are used to determine the mass of C and H respectively. The quantity of oxygen present is calculated from the difference between the sample mass and the mass of C and H determined to be present.

Many organic compounds also contain additional elements such as NITROGEN, SULFUR, and HALOGEN. The presence of any of these elements is clearly shown by instrumental techniques. It can also be determined by a chemical technique called sodium fusion.

Sodium fusion involves reaction between the organic sample and sodium vapor. This drastic process causes the organic compound to be charred, usually resulting in carbon, some carbon dioxide, and the conversion of organically bonded N,S, and X to the ionic $C{\equiv}N-$, S^{2-}, and X^{1-}. These water soluble sodium salts can then be identified by appropriate precipitation reactions.

$$N,S,X \quad {-}{-}Na(g){-}{-}{-}> \quad NaC{\equiv}N, \ Na_2S, \ NaX$$

The excess sodium is destroyed by reaction first with alcohol and then with water.

$$2Na \ + \ 2EtOH \ {-}{-}{-}{-}{-}> \ 2NaOEt + H_2$$
$$\text{and}$$
$$2Na \ + \ 2H_2O \ {-}{-}{-}{-}{-}> \ 2NaOH \ + \ H_2$$

This results in an alkaline solution of the sodium salts. This solution is filtered to yield a stock solution for the individual tests.

(1) The presence of SULFUR is confirmed by the formation of a BLACK PRECIPITATE when acidified stock solution is reacted with lead acetate.

$$S^{2-} \ + \ Pb^{2+} \ {-}{-}{-}{-}{-}> \ PbS{\downarrow}$$

(2) The presence of NITROGEN is confirmed by formation of the Prussian blue color of ferric ferrocyanide.

a) $6C{\equiv}N^- \ + \ Fe^{2+} \ {-}{-}{-}> \ [Fe(CN)_6]^{4-}$

b) $4Fe^{3+} \ + \ 3[Fe(CN)_6]^{4-} \ {-}{-}{-}> \ Fe_4[Fe(CN)_6]_3$

(3) The presence of HALOGEN is confirmed by reaction of stock solution with silver nitrate. This test requires the removal of CN^- and of S^{-2}.

$$X^- \ + \ Ag^+ \ ---> \ AgX \downarrow$$

Thus the presence of various elements, other than C,H,0 can be determined by performing a sodium fusion test followed by the qualitative analysis of the resulting ionic salts.

PROCEDURE

The procedure given is for the analysis of an unknown. Usually, the same procedure is carried out simultaneously using a known sample which contains all three elements to be tested. In this way, a positive confirmatory test can be placed next to the same test for an unknown for comparison purposes.

I. Preparation of stock solution.

NOTE: Sodium fusion involves highly reactive substances. There is often danger of loud popping or explosion. Thus, this must be done in the HOOD. The hood window should be pulled down and safety goggles and gloves must be worn. Sodium is dangerous to handle because it reacts with water and water vapor. It is usually stored under kerosene.

1. Clamp a clean, dry 13 x 100 mm test tube to a ring stand in the HOOD so that the tube is in the vertical position. Put on a pair of gloves and then cut a piece (about the size of a small pea) of sodium metal using a sharp spatula or scissors. Dry this piece of metal using filter paper. Then, using forceps, transfer this sodium to the clean test tube in the hood.

NOTE: if any small pieces of sodium remain on the gloves or filter paper, they must be destroyed by treatment with ethanol.

2. Light a Bunsen burner and pass the flame along the sides of the tube several times to drive out any water vapor. Then begin to heat the bottom of the tube until the sodium melts and begins to form thick gray vapor in the (lower 1/5 of the test tube. Once the vapor has formed, the organic compound to be fused can be added.

3. Remove the flame, and QUICKLY but CAUTIOUSLY, add FOUR DROPS of any liquid unknown or about 0.2g of any solid unknown to the sodium vapor. Try to add the compound so that it falls directly on the vapor and not on the sides of the test tube. A violent reaction should take place.

4. Heat the tube to redness for at least one minute to complete the sodium fusion process. Allow the tube to cool to room temperature.

5. Then add about 3-mLs of ethanol in 5-drop increments. After each addition, stir the mixture and break up the charred material as much as possible. This destroys excess unreacted sodium.

6. Add 1-mL of distilled water to the test tube and stir well. Place an additional 5-mLs of distilled water in a 50-mL beaker. Then, hold the test-tube over the beaker. Use a metal spatula to crack the bottom of the test tube so that the contents spill into the water in the beaker. This should dissolve all the fused salts and completely react any remaining sodium.

7. Filter this solution into a 50-mL Erlenmeyer using a glass funnel. The liquid obtained is the stock solution which will be used in the qualitative test for each element. Discard the solids and the broken glass in an appropriate container.

II. Qualitative Tests

1. SULFUR TEST

Place about 2-mLs of the stock solution in a reaction tube. Add dilute acetic acid ($\approx$ 5%) until the solution is acidic to pH or litmus paper. Add 5 drops of 5% lead acetate solution. A black precipitate indicates the presence of sulfur.

If the solution is dark brown in color, allow the tube to sit for several minutes. Then check the bottom for the precipitate.

Record the results.

2. NITROGEN TEST

Place about 3-mLs of the stock solution in a medium test tube. Add 5 drops of 5% ferrous sulfate (freshly prepared) and 5 drops of 10% KF. [The potassium fluoride is added to increase the sensitivity of this test.]

Boil the mixture gently for about twenty seconds. Cool.

Add 2 drops of 5% ferric chloride.

Add 25% H_2SO_4 in 5-drop increments until all iron hydroxide precipitates dissolve. Make sure the solution is acidic to pH paper or to litmus paper.

If nitrogen is present, a brilliant blue color appears. It may be in solution or as a suspension. If a greenish-blue color is obtained, the fusion process was incomplete but nitrogen is present.

Record the results.

3. HALOGEN TEST

Place about 3-mLs of the stock solution in a medium test tube. Add dilute HNO_3 until the solution is acidic to pH paper or to litmus paper.

If sulfur or nitrogen (or both) are present in the unknown, boil vigorously on the sand bath in the HOOD for about five minutes. This serves to drive out H_2S and HCN vapor. If the solution is not boiled long enough, S^{-2} and $C\equiv N^-$ will remain. These ions react with silver ion to form black precipitates which obscure the test for halogens.

To the remaining liquid, add 4 to five drops of silver nitrate solution.

The formation of a white, tan, or yellow precipitate indicates the presence of a halogen.

AgCl = white; AgBr = tan or cream; AgI = yellow

Record the results.

EXPERIMENT 30: Report and Worksheet

ELEMENTAL ANALYSIS BY SODIUM FUSION

Student Name: _____   Day: _____

Student Number: _____   Date: _____

_____

DATA

	KNOWN TEST APPEARANCE	UNKNOWN TEST APPEARANCE
1. Sulfur Test		
2. Nitrogen Test		
3. Halogen Test		

UNKNOWN NUMBER _____

ELEMENTS PRESENT:

QUESTIONS

am sample of a hydrocarbon is combusted to form CO_2 and H_2O. water obtained is 0.0384 gram. The mass of carbon dioxide 692 grams. In this analysis, all the carbon in the original sample to carbon dioxide and all the hydrogen is converted to water. Calculate the percentage of each element present in the original hydrocarbon. Calculate the empirical formula of the hydrocarbon.

2. What happens to an organic molecule when it undergoes sodium fusion?

3. What is the appearance of and the equation for each confirmatory test?

(a) SULFUR

(b) NITROGEN

(c) HALOGEN

Notes